NEW SIX O'CLOCK SAINTS

NEW SIX O'CLOCK SAINTS

by JOAN WINDHAM

with illustrations by

Caryll Houselander

New York

Sheed & Ward, Inc.

Manufactured in the United States of America
By The Haddon Craftsmen, Scranton, Pa.

CONTENTS

	PAGE
St. William	1
St. Irene	7
St. Kenneth	14
St. Veronica	20
St. Walter	26
St. Humphrey	33
St. Stephen	40
St. Alice	45
St. Jennifer	52
St. Mungo	58
St. Owen	66
St. David	74
St. Ronald	83
St. Joseph of Arimathea	92
St. Gladys	98

ST. WILLIAM

O NCE upon a time there was a man called William, and he was French, and he lived in the Country. One day he had some business to see to in Paris (which is the Capital of France), so he put on his Blue Velvet clothes and he saddled his Bay Horse and he rode into Town. Now the Business took so long that William thought that he would stay the night, and finish the next morning, so he went to an Hotel, and the Hotel man put the Bay Horse in the Stable and showed William his room. After supper William thought that he would go out for a walk before going to bed, so as to have a Look Round Paris.

The Extraordinary Thing was that although there were Churches and things in Paris, nearly everybody had stopped being Christians, and were Pagans, and Shocking Wicked ones they were! William's eyes got rounder and bigger as he walked about. He couldn't *believe* what he saw and heard!

"*Well!*" he said to himself, "well, I *say*! Good gracious me!" And he hurried back to his Hotel and went to bed.

Next day, when his Business was done, he rode home on the Bay Horse, and all the time he couldn't help thinking about the Wickedness of Paris. He simply couldn't Get Over it at all.

Then he thought this thought:

"Supposing I go and be a Hermit, and use all my time praying and things—I wonder if it would help to make up to God for all the Wickedness of the people of Paris? They are so Horrible to God that they don't even

1

remember that He died for them. Imagine Dying for somebody and they don't even remember that you did it!"

So he went home and gave his house and garden and things to his Family and said Good-bye to them, and went off to be a Hermit. He learned a lot about God all by himself in his little Cell, and every day he told Him how sorry he was about the People of Paris.

One day God said to William:

"William, I want you to go to the Abbey at Citeaux, where St. Bernard was. You would be able to do more things for me there, and you would have the Church and the Blessed Sacrament nice and near."

So William went to Citeaux, and soon he was the Abbot there, and then he was made the Archbishop of Bourges, which is a town in France. (An Archbishop is a Top kind of Bishop, like an Archangel is a Top kind of Angel and an Archduke is the Top kind of Duke in Austria.)

Now in his Secret Self William always wanted to be a poor Hermit and not a rich Archbishop, and so, although he had to wear Soft Clothing and live in a Palace because of his Rank, he stayed very poor and humble inside, so as to be as much like a Hermit as he could Notwithstanding, and he worked hard and got up early. (Like the Pope does, and like the King does.)

One day a priest called Gerald came to see William.

"Please, Your Grace," he said, "may I speak to you about something Important?"

"Certainly, Father, what is it?" said William kindly.

"Well," said Father Gerald, "my right hand has Gone Lame, and I can't use it at all."

"So what?" said William.

"So I can't say Mass any more," said Father Gerald.

"Oh," said William, "how lucky for you."

"*Lucky!*" said Father Gerald. "Did you say *Lucky?*"

"Yes, I said Lucky," said William.

"Why?" said Father Gerald.

"Well," said William, "you go to Confession this evening and to Holy Communion to-morrow morning, and then come back to me and I'll tell you. Or perhaps you will tell me!"

So Father Gerald went to Confession in the evening and to Holy Communion in the morning, and then he went to see William again.

"Good morning, Your Grace," he said. "Please may I speak to you about something Important?"

"What is it?" asked William.

"Well," said Father Gerald, "I did what you said, and now I want to know something."

"What do you want to know?" said William.

"How did you know that I had a Mortal Sin?" said Father Gerald. "It's really most Mysterious!"

"*Had* you got a Mortal Sin?" said William. "Well, then, it *was* Lucky that you had a Lame Hand, wasn't it?"

"Yes, it was," said Father Gerald. "How *very* Kind of God to make me so that I couldn't possibly say Mass when I'd got a Mortal Sin!"

"It would have been a Terrible Thing," said William, "for you to say Mass and hold the Blessed Sacrament in your hands when you had a Mortal Sin. It would have been making God, who is Clean and Beautiful, come near to your Dirty, Ugly, Stuffy Soul. Can you *Imagine* it?"

"My hand is a little better," said Father Gerald.

"In three days' time," said William, "when you have told God how sorry you are, it will be as Good as New."

And it was, and Father Gerald could say Mass **again**, which was very kind indeed of God.

William was a very Cheerful man, and he was always Singing or Laughing, and lots of Rather Po-faced People disapproved of him.

"Why are you always Singing and Laughing?" they asked him. "You ought to be Grave and Solemn when you are an Archbishop."

"Why?" asked William in a Surprised voice.

"Because Archbishops are supposed to be near to God, and so they ought to be Solemn," they said, and they looked at William as though they couldn't think how he ever came to be an Archbishop at all.

"But it is a Happy thing to be near to God," said William, laughing at them. "It is a Lovely thing, and a Glad thing, and I couldn't be Solemn and Grave."

But the people went away shaking their heads. They were the sort of people who go to Damp Churches that smell of Mothball on Sundays, wearing their Black Clothes. Then they lock up the Churches so that no one can get in on all the Other Days, which is all very Stuck Up and Stuffy.

One of the things that these people were always doing was a Sin called Detraction, which is Telling Tales. Now this was William's Favourite Sin to Hate, and he was always telling them about it.

"Now listen, all you people," he used to say, "if you say that Mrs. Popinjay drinks her Bathwater and spills her food down her Front when it isn't True, well that's a sin, because it is Telling Lies about poor Mrs. Popinjay. But it doesn't matter Terribly because she can laugh and say: "What nonsense!" and all her friends can say: "What a shame! Of *course* she doesn't!" And so Mrs. Popinjay isn't Miserable, only Cross.

But if it *is* True, then it is downright Wicked to say so. First, it is none of your Business if she does drink her Bathwater, even if it is a Grubby thing to do; and Second, no one else might know about it, and Mrs. Popinjay might be trying very hard to stop doing it (she might even have actually stopped). Then if you tell everyone about it they will say, "No! Does she *really*? How awful of her! *Well* now! And they will tell everyone else and poor Mrs. Popinjay will be *Miserable* because everybody knows about her Grubby Tricks, and she may even have to go away and live somewhere else all because of you! So that Detraction is one of the *Meanest* things," said William. And you can see that he was quite right, can't you?

One day William thought this thought:

"I think I'd like to be a Missionary now, and tell all the people who don't know about God. I'll tell them about Our Lord at Christmas and at Easter and about Our Lady and about the Sacraments, and all, and they'll be Delighted to hear such Good News!"

So he packed up some things ready to start. He took some Camping things, and a Roll-up Bed like soldiers have, and a Kettle and a Cup and a Plate and things, and a Crucifix and a statue of Our Lady to show to the Heathen people, and some Writing things so that he could write home and tell the Others how he was getting on. He worked for two whole days packing up, and when everything was downstairs in the hall ready to start in the morning he went to bed. He was very Tired.

While he was asleep his Guardian Angel came and said:

"Wake up, William. I want to tell you something!"

"What will you tell me?" asked William, rubbing his eyes. He was still very tired after all the Packing, and he could hardly keep his eyes open.

"It is time to stop living in that Tired old body of yours, and come and live with us," said the Guardian Angel.

"Die, do you mean?" asked William in an Interested voice.

"Yes," said the Guardian Angel; "die here and live there."

"But What about being a Missionary?" said William.

"Wouldn't you rather live with God?" said the Guardian Angel; "you are always so happy when he is near you."

"Oh *yes!*" said William, "I'd rather do that than Anything at all. I was thinking of the Ages and Ages of Purgatory I should have to have first," said poor old William. "When can we start?"

"I don't think you will have any Purgatory," said the Guardian Angel, and he helped William to stand up, and held his arm. "God loves you very much, and you have always been a poor Hermit inside. We can start now."

And William went away with his Guardian Angel, and there was God waiting for him and smiling at him for being such a Happy man.

So when someone came in the morning to tell William that it was time to get up he found that he had gone already, so someone else went to be the Missionary, so as not to waste all that Packing.

There are lots of other St. Williams, and most of them are English, so I thought that I'd tell you about this one who is French. His Special Day is on January 10th, and people called William are all over the World.

ST. IRENE

(Now this Story isn't at all Exciting, but it is very Interesting, because it is about Two Plans. And at the end you will be able to choose which of the Two Plans you like best.)

ONCE upon a time there was a Princess of Hungary, and her name was Princess Irene, and she married a man called John the Beautiful, because he was so Handsome.

After their Honeymoon, and when they had settled down at home, Princess Irene and John the Beautiful were sitting in the Garden after breakfast. They were throwing bits of bread to the birds and talking about the different ways that they could Know and Love and Serve God in this world, and be happy with him forever in the next world (which is Heaven).

"I do think that we ought to make some sort of a Plan," said Irene, and she threw an extra fat piece of bread to a Rather Shy bird.

"Well, we both love God more than anyone else," said John the Beautiful, "so I should think that to start with we could build a Chapel in the garden. Then we could live very near the Blessed Sacrament, and be able to go and visit Our Lord lots of times a day, so that He could help us with the Plan if we got in a Muddle."

"Yes, let's do that first," said Irene. "Some people," she said, "are Monks and Nuns and spend *all* their time for God, and have nothing at all for themselves."

"But *we* couldn't," said John the Beautiful, "because we are Married."

"Well, we could if we both wanted to and the Pope said we could," said Irene.

"But we don't want to," said John the Beautiful, "and God *likes* people to be married, and to live in their houses, and garden in their gardens, and have children in the nursery, and look after their dogs and things."

"But perhaps He would rather that they were Monks and Nuns," said Irene, "because it is so happy to be married that people might forget God."

"It couldn't really be like that," said John the Beautiful, "because God specially made Two Sacraments for the way we live. One of them is Marriage, so that people can use and enjoy all the things that God has invented for them, and have children so that they can know about God, too. The other one is Holy Orders, which is Priests and Nuns and things, who give up everything in the world for a Sacrifice, and spend all their time for God. People can choose which way they will live. God likes to have some of each."

"Oh, yes," said Princess Irene, "and the Two Sorts can't do without each other. The people with Holy Orders, like Priests, teach us and give us the Sacraments, and the Monks and Nuns pray for the people who forget to pray for themselves, so we couldn't get on without *them*."

"And the Marriage people," said John the Beautiful, "grow the food and make the clothes and the machinery, and build the houses and the Churches and have the children, and all that, so of Course we couldn't do without *them*!"

"Well," said Irene, "we can serve God just as much when we are married, but not in the same way as the people in Holy Orders."

"Of course we can," said John the Beautiful. "God

The people ran out and waved to John . . .

made the world and everything in it for us to enjoy. All the things in it remind us of Him, and so we go on loving Him more and more."

"Don't let us both have the same Plan," said Irene; "let's be different, and then we'll be able to tell each other how we get on."

"All right," said John the Beautiful, and so it was settled.

John's Plan was that he would Serve God by doing things for His people. (Because you remember that God said that if you do things for people because you love God, then God counts that as doing it for Him.) So John farmed his farms and gardened in his garden and sailed in his boat and rode his horses and did it all because God is Good. He gave his extra milk and corn to poor people who hadn't got any. And he grew extra vegetables and flowers and gave them to the Hospital, and he sailed his boat because God has made the Sea and the Wind and the Sun so strong that John thought that it just showed how Strong God must be. And that made him so happy that he used to sing louder than the Wind and the Waves. And he built the Chapel in the garden, so that he and Irene could go to Holy Communion every morning, and hear what God had to say to them.

All the people in the village loved John the Beautiful, and they liked to see him riding by on his big horse, and they all ran out and waved to him as he passed, and John thought to himself:

"They can't all be running out just to see *me*. It must be my Big Shining Horse." And so he polished his harness and put shining Silver medals on it, and put Ribbons in his horse's mane, so that the people would have something to look at. Then he put on a Golden Silk Cloak and rode through the Village. All the people clapped and cheered, not because of the Horses and the Cloak, but because they loved John. But he never thought of that, because he was thinking about how good God is.

"Well!" said John when he got home, "that *was* a Success! I think I'd better put on splendid clothes every time I go out to see about Roofs and Drains and Extra Milk and things." And he did, and he went about Enjoying everything.

"It would be disappointing for God," he thought, "when He makes all these things and no one even Notices them. And I must say God has given me everything, because no one could have nicer neighbours than I have, and no one *could* have a nicer Wife than my Princess Irene."

Now Irene was Shy, and she didn't want to Serve God by serving her neighbours, because she never knew what to say to them, and so she made a different Plan.

"I know what I will do," she said. "I will spend all my Spare Time with God so as to make up to Him for all the people who forget Him. And I will collect all the Sacrifices I can, and give them to Him to try to make up for all that He had done for us."

So Irene used to wear Rather Plain clothes so that no one would notice her, and she used to Sew and Knit things for the Poor-and-Raggies, and she used to send food and fruit and cake and soup and things to the Hospital, and all that. But no one ever knew who did the knitting and the sewing.

Irene was very busy in her house, because she had some children, and she made their clothes, and she made the jam and she stored the fruit, and all the time she gave all her work to God, and when she got tired she gave Him her tiredness for a Sacrifice. And always she thought how kind God was to give her such a nice Family.

"No one could have nicer children than I have," she said, "and no one *could* have such a good and Handsome Husband." And all through the day, whenever she had a minute to spare, she used to visit the Blessed Sacrament, and God told her things. But whenever John went Sailing, Irene went, too, because she loved the Sun and the Wind.

Irene used to sew and knit for the Poor-and-Raggies.

After supper John and Irene used to compare notes, and tell each other about the things that they had been doing.

"Your way is best, though," said Irene to John, "because you make so many people happy."

"No, *your* way is best," said John the Beautiful, "because all your ornaments are inside, and all the things that you do are secrets between you and God. Our Lord said that we ought to do it like that, and lay up Treasure in Heaven."

"Anyway, whosesoever way is the best, you are the nicest person in the world," said Princess Irene.

"No, you are!" said John the Beautiful, and they both laughed.

I wonder which Plan you like best? It doesn't matter which, because there have to be some of each.

St. Irene's Special Day is on August 13th, and anyone who has her Birthday on that day, as well as all the Irenes, can have her for their Special Saint.

ST. KENNETH

ONCE upon a time there was a Welsh Village Woman who had a baby son, just born. But the Prince who ruled that village had a Wife, and she *hadn't* got a son. The Prince knew she would be furiously jealous if she heard that a mere Village Woman had one. So to save trouble, the Prince did a very Heartless thing. He told the Village Woman to throw away the baby and say nothing about it.

"Throw it away!" said the Village Woman. "Do you mean really Throw it Away like rubbish?"

"Throw it on the Rubbish Heap or throw it in the Sea," said the Welsh Prince. "I don't mind which you do, but I never want to see or hear of it again. Here is some money for you." And he went away.

The poor Village Woman was in a Great Way; because, after all, it was her baby, and she liked it. But she was afraid of what the Welsh Prince might do to her if she disobeyed him, and so this is what she did:

First she took the baby to the Church to be Baptised, and his name was Kenneth. Then she took him home and put a label on a string round his neck with "My name is Kenneth" written on it. Then she wrapped him up in a warm woolly shawl and thought to herself:

"I *couldn't* put him on the Rubbish Heap, poor little Kenneth, so I'll have to throw him in the Sea," and she picked him up and she carried him down to the Beach, and all the time she cried and cried it was so Sad.

Just as she was going to put him into the cold Sea she saw a round Fisherman's Boat called a Coracle, like Alan

14

. . . they each pulled out a few feathers.

sailed to see St. Columba in, and she dragged it down to the water and put Kenneth in it.

"Never mind whose it is," she thought to herself; "they wouldn't mind if they knew why I took it."

And she pushed the coracle farther and farther out to Sea until the water was too Deep for her to go another step. Then she shut her eyes and gave it one last push and turned back to the beach. When she was standing on the sand she turned round and saw the coracle bobbing away out to Sea, but she couldn't see Kenneth, because he was lying in the bottom of it. She sniffed sadly, and walked home to change her wet things.

Kenneth, in his coracle, floated away down the Coast until he reached the Gower Peninsula, and there he was washed ashore. Even now the Gower Coast is very wild and lonely, so it must have been even lonelier in those days. He hadn't been lying there very long when a Most Unusual thing happened, and this is what it was.

A whole flock of Seagulls came, and each of them took a little piece of the woolly shawl in its beak. Then they all flew up together and carried Kenneth to a wide ledge like a Grassy Shelf high up on the Cliff. And what is more they flew down and brought up the coracle as well. Then they all sat in a ring round the edge of the coracle and they each pulled out a few feathers, and soon there was a lovely warm nest for Kenneth. They lifted him in, and then flew away screaming and crying, like Seagulls always do.

Not long after this a Deer came along the top of the Cliff with her calf. Suddenly she pricked up her ears and stopped dead. The calf stopped so suddenly that he skidded on all four feet and bumped into her. She stared over the edge of the cliff, and there, just below her, was Kenneth in his coracle. Now the Deer didn't know about

People because of the Gower Coast being so Wild and lonely, but she did know that this was a Baby Something, and she was a mother Deer with a Baby of her own.

"Poor little thing," she thought. "I have quite enough milk for two, but how shall I get to that other Baby?"

Just then a still More Unusual thing happened, and an Angel came along the cliff carrying a Silver Bell. He put the Silver Bell upside down in the coracle and went away.

"The very thing!" thought the Deer, and she put some milk in the Bell and Kenneth turned over and saw it. He took hold of it and the milk tipped over his face, and so he learned to drink! Every day the Deer came and gave him some milk, and he began to grow and get strong.

One day a Good Shepherd came walking along the cliff edge looking for Sheep that had fallen over and might want helping back again. From far away he saw something moving, and he thought:

"There is one of my Sheep! It does not look as though it could get back over the Top very easily. I'd better go along and help it."

But when he got there he saw a fine Fat Baby crawling about in the sun! He stared and stared!

"Well, upon my Sam!" he said. "Whoever saw the like of that!"

He climbed over the edge of the cliff and tried to pick up Kenneth. But he was a real little Wild Baby, because he had never seen a person before that he could remember, and so he crawled away into a little cave where he sheltered in Bad Weather. However, the Shepherd fished him out with his Crook (like Bishops have because of Feed My Sheep and because of Our Lord being the Good Shepherd) and he put him on his shoulder like a Lamb and climbed back to the top of the cliff.

When he got home he wrapped up Kenneth in his cloak and went indoors.

"Guess what I have here, Wife!" he said to his wife. She looked at the Wriggling Bundle.

"I should think that it is a Cosset Lamb for me to bring up, same as usual," she said. (A Cosset Lamb is a Lamb whose mother is dead, so that it has to be looked after and have a Baby's Bottle and all that. Some people call them Pet Lambs, but there is no difference.)

"No, it isn't," said the Shepherd.

"Well, it's *something* small and wriggling," said his wife, "and I suppose that it is for me, or you wouldn't have brought it in. Extraordinary thing, it makes noises just like a Baby!"

"That's right!" said the Shepherd, and he Roared with Laughter.

"What's right?" said his wife, and she took hold of the cloak and out rolled wriggling little Kenneth!

"Goodness gracious me!" said the Shepherd's wife, all Astonished. "Whose is he?"

And the Shepherd told her all about how he had found Kenneth, and about how they had better keep him and bring him up Properly.

"Good!" said the Shepherd's wife. "I've always wanted a Baby, and now I've got one. Look! his name's Kenneth, it says so on the label."

So she washed and fed Kenneth, and wrapped him up, and put him outside the Cottage to go to sleep.

But the Seagulls saw him! They all swooped down and lifted him up to take him back to the Cliff, because they were used to seeing him there. But a Very Dangerous Thing happened. Kenneth was much older and heavier than he was the last time, and he kicked and wriggled, and the Seagulls dropped him! Kenneth lay at the end of the Garden and screamed and screamed.

The Shepherd's wife came running out, and when she picked him up she found that he had a Broken Leg! Now there were no good Doctors in those days, and so forever afterwards Kenneth had a Lame Leg, and he Limped.

The Shepherd and his wife brought up Kenneth just as if he were their own child, and he went to School, and he learned his Catechism and all that, but when he grew up he was a Hermit, and he lived on the same ledge with the little Cave that he had had when he was a Baby. He taught the people all about God in Nature, because of the Seagulls and the Deer that had been so kind to him, and because of the beautiful View that he could see from his Cave, and every Sunday he used to go to the Parish Church and help the Priest there by doing all the Catechism Classes for him. And all the people loved the kind old man with a Lame Leg who lived all alone on the Cliff.

St. Kenneth's Special Day is on August 1st, and there are a lot of Kenneths.

ST. VERONICA

ONCE upon a time there was a Horse Dealer who was an Honest Man. Whenever he had a horse to sell that was not quite Perfect (perhaps it had a Hard Mouth, or was a bit Nappy, or Shied, or was Galled or something), then he always Mentioned it to the customer in case he might not want a horse like that. Well, this horse dealer was very poor, because he didn't sell many horses, and he had a Daughter called Veronica.

Veronica was a very nice girl, but she couldn't read or write, because her father was too poor for her to go to school, and so she used to go out Weeding to earn a little money. Weeding is rather a tiring job, but Veronica liked it because it was nice and peaceful, and gave her time to think about God. The more she thought, the more she wanted to be a Nun, and at last one day she said to her Mother:

"Mummy, I *do* want to be a Nun. Do you think I could?"

"No, darling," said her Mother, "you couldn't because you can't read or write, and we can't Afford to send you to School." And she went on getting the supper ready.

Poor Veronica was very Disappointed. And every night she used to go to bed early with her candle (they hadn't got any other kind of light), and she used to try to learn her Letters and how to Write.

But it is very difficult to learn your letters if there is no one to help you. I am sure that you find it quite hard enough even though there is always someone to ask.

One night she worked at her reading and writing until

. . . there was Our Lady, looking at the Letters.

her candle burned out and she put her head on the table and cried!

"I'll *never* know my letters!" she sobbed sadly, and she rubbed her eyes. "And if I don't I can never read or write, and then I can never be a Nun!" And she rubbed her nose.

All of a Sudden the room got light again without the candle, and there was Our Lady, looking at the Letters.

"You Never mind, Veronica," said Our Lady, "you don't have to know all these letters. Now, I'll help you! You only need to know Three Letters, a White Letter, and a Black Letter, and a Red Letter."

"I didn't know that letters had Colours," said Veronica, sniffing and drying her eyes.

"These have," said Our Lady. "Now Listen. The White Letter is TRUTH. You must *tell* the Truth and *think* the truth and *do* the truth. That's easy, isn't it?"

"Yes," said Veronica in an Interested voice.

"The Black Letter is CONTENT. You must be contented wherever God puts you, and never take Offence if He gives you a Humble job. If He wants you to Weed then you must want to Weed and not want to be an Industrial Magnate or something. If God wants you to be a Nun, you'll be one, never fear."

"Yes," said Veronica, nodding her head up and down.

"Now the Red Letter," said Our Lady. "The Red Letter is for Our Lord's PASSION. You must learn how to think about all the things that Our Lord did, but especially about all the terrible things that happened to Him before he died for us all. Learn all you can about these three Letters and the others will come in time." And she went away.

Veronica learned the Three Letters for a long time,

and then she went to a Convent and asked the Reverend Mother if she could please be a Nun.

"Well," said the Reverend Mother, "but you won't be able to do much, will you, if you can't read or write?"

"No," said Veronica sadly, "I wouldn't be much help, I'm afraid." And she turned to go away again. Just as she got to the door the Reverend Mother said:

"Veronica, if you were a Nun here would you go into the streets and Beg for us?" Veronica stopped.

"Beg in the Streets?" she thought. "We have always been poor, but we have never done that!" And she was just going to say very Politely to the Reverend Mother that she really didn't think that she *could*, when she remembered the Black Letter (do you?) and she said:

"Yes, Reverend Mother, I would certainly Beg for you if you told me to."

And so Veronica at last had the thing that she had wanted for so long, and she was a Nun. And every day she used to go out into the Streets and beg from door to door. Sometimes people gave her something, but more often they said:

"What, you Cadging round here again? Some people don't know what to do with their time!" And they would Slam the door and leave Veronica outside.

And when that happened Veronica would remember the Black Letter and try next door.

Now because of the Coloured Letters Veronica began to know a great deal about God, but she was very Shy about letting the other Nuns know about the kind of things that God did for her, in case they thought she was Boasting (which is blowing your Own Trumpet).

One day, on the Feast of Corpus Christi, all the Nuns were at Mass. The priest had just got to the part where he lifts up the Host for everybody to see (called the

Elevation), when a wonderful thing happened. There at the Altar was the Baby Jesus with Three Angels! Veronica stared and stared, and she was so happy to see such a thing that she smiled an enormous Smile. After Mass, when they were all coming out of the Chapel, she said to one of the other Nuns:

"Wasn't that a Wonderful Thing?"

"What was?" said the other Nun.

"Didn't you see the Baby Jesus?" said Veronica in a Surprised voice.

"No," said the other Nun, staring at her, "did you?"

But Veronica got Shy and rather red and Embarrassed, and she didn't say any more. She knew that God had let her be the only one to see Him.

Veronica was very sad because she couldn't sing Office with the other Nuns (because of not being able to read and write), and she kept telling God how sorry she was to be so stupid. One evening she was sitting in her room while all the other Nuns were singing Vespers and Compline, and she looked at her Office book, and she tried to read it but she couldn't.

"You sing it with me," said a voice just behind her, "and you will find that it isn't so difficult after all!"

Veronica turned round. She was very surprised, because she thought that all the others were in Chapel and that she was alone. But it wasn't another Nun at all; it was her Guardian Angel! And they both sang Vespers and Compline, and Veronica did find that it wasn't so difficult as she had thought that it was.

After that her Guardian Angel came every evening; and once, when she was ill, the Nun who looked after the ill ones saw a light under Veronica's door.

"That naughty Sister Veronica!" said the Nun. "She ought to be asleep, with that Bad Cold she's got!" And she went to Veronica's room to turn out the light. But when she got there she heard Singing!

"Well now!" she thought, "Sister Veronica doesn't know how to sing Vespers. I wonder who can be in there with her?" and she opened the door very quietly. There was Veronica, sitting up in bed and singing Vespers. But the Nun who was looking after her couldn't see the Guardian Angel, and she shut the door carefully again.

"I don't know what to make of it at all," she said to herself as she made some Bread and Milk for Veronica's supper. "It's all Very Queer."

St. Veronica's Special Day is on January 13th. There are some other Veronicas, but I told you about this one because her father was a Horse Dealer.

There was the Baby Jesus with Three Angels!

ST. WALTER

ONCE upon a time there was a Noble Knight and his name was Sir Walter, and he was a Crusader, and he fought the Saracens (who were Infidels) in the Holy Land (which was where Our Lord used to live).

Walter's favourite person of all was Our Lady, and he had a little Ivory Statue of Her. "Other people have a Master to work for," he used to say, "but I have a Mistress, and I am Her Servant."

One day Walter was going to fight in a Tournament, which is a Pretence Battle. All the Knights dressed in their best Armour and rode their best Horses, and they had coloured Feathers in their Helmets and Silk Cloaks to match, and Flags and all that. And they had a Battle Field with seats all round it, and all the Ladies used to go in their Best Clothes and watch. Then, at the end, the most Important Lady (sometimes it was the Queen), gave a prize to the knight who had fought Best of All. The Knights used to wear a Ribbon or a Handkerchief belonging to their Favourite Lady because they said that it brought them luck, and so the Ribbons and things were called Favours. Walter always wore a Blue Favour, because of Our Lady's Favourite colour being Blue.

Well, on this day that I am telling you about, Walter and a lot of his friends were riding to the Tournament with their Colours, and their shining Horses clattering along the road, and they were all talking and laughing because they were going to have such a jolly day, and they all hoped that they would be the one to Win the

Prize. As they were riding along they passed a little Chapel ringing its bell for Mass. Walter stopped.

"I'll just hear Mass on the way," he said, "because it is one of the Feasts of Our Lady, and she is my Special Person."

Some of the Knights turned round and came back to see what was going on.

"But, Walter, you'll be late for the Tournament!" said one of the Knights, who wore a Scarlet Cloak.

"Yes, Walter, now do come along; you can go to Mass to-morrow instead!" said another Knight, in a Yellow Cloak.

"No," said Walter. "My Mistress comes first. But I will leave when we get to the Last Gospel, and I won't wait for the prayers at the end. I don't think I'll be very Late!"

So all the other Knights went on to the Tournament and Walter tied up his horse to a nearby Tree and went in to Mass.

After the Last Gospel he came out and untied his horse and rode away to the pretence Battle Field. When he had nearly got there he met some Knights coming away from it, all talking in Excited Voices.

"Good morning!" said Walter. "How is the Tournament going?"

"It is nearly over," said one of the Knights, who was wearing a Purple Cloak. "Sir Walter has carried away all the Honours! No Knight has ever fought so well before. He is a wonderful man! If you hurry you might just see him before he goes home." And they rode on.

Walter was All Astonished.

"What *did* they mean?" he said to himself. "I wasn't there at all!" And he went in to the Battle Field where the Tournament was.

The Pretence Battle was just finished, and as he sat on his horse in his Sky Blue Cloak some Knights who were pretence Prisoners of the battle came to him and said:

"Be kind to your Prisoners, Sir Walter. We had no Idea that you could fight so well!"

"But I wasn't there!" said Walter. And he made a Puzzled face. "You are not *my* Prisoners!"

He sat on his horse in his Sky Blue Cloak.

And the prisoners all laughed, because they thought that Walter was Making a Joke!

What do you suppose had really happened? Our Lady had sent an Angel, looking exactly like Sir Walter, Sky Blue cloak and all, to take his place in the pretence Battle while he was at Mass. Which was very kind of Her because he won the Prize.

Walter was so pleased and thankful to Our Lady for being so good to him that he thought that he would go and be a Cistercian Monk (like St. Bernard) so as to have more time for God. And so he went, and the only thing that he took with him was the little Ivory Statue of Our Lady. When he got there the head monk said:

"Well, Walter, you may certainly come and be a monk, but you can't be a priest, because you don't know any Latin."

"I know, Father," said Walter sadly. "But you see I was brought up to be a Knight and a Soldier, and so I only had to learn enough to be able to follow Mass and all that. I had to learn a lot about fighting and farming and landlording and all that."

"You will have to be a Lay Brother and look after the Vineyards then," said the Abbot; "that will be more in your line." And that is what Walter did, and very fine grapes he grew. You see, one of the ways that these monks Earned their Living was to grow a great many grapes, and they made a very good Wine out of them. and they sold it to all the people round about, and so they got the money to buy the things they needed.

Now in Monasteries and Convents they always Read Aloud at meal times so that the monks or nuns don't think too much about what they eat and perhaps get Greedy, and they nearly always read in Latin, because they all know it. If they read in English the French or German ones might not understand, and if they read in French or German then the English or the Italian ones might not understand. (That is one reason why Mass is in Latin, did you know? When you are bigger you will know and understand all the words, and then you can go to Mass in France and the words will all be in Latin, and you will know it even if you can't speak French, and

that will be nice and homely for you, and the same in
Germany or Poland. And the same for the Foreigners
who come to us.)

Well, Walter hadn't learned much Latin, but at the
Reading aloud at meal times sometimes he smiled and
sometimes he nearly cried, and always he looked interested.

So the Abbot said:

"Brother Walter, why do you Smile or nearly cry
when you can't understand what we are reading
about?"

"No, Father Abbot," said Walter, "I am not smiling
at that book, but I have an Imaginary Picture Book
(Imaginary is Pretence) and I imagine a picture of Our
Lord when He was born, and then I turn over a page and
I imagine Him in St. Joseph's Carpenter's shop, and then
I turn over another page and I see a picture of Him being
Crucified. I see pictures of all the things that happened
to Him in my Imaginary Picture Book."

"Oh, I see!" said the Abbot. "Well, that is all right;
I only wondered."

One day the Abbot said to Walter:

"Brother Walter, the grapes that you have grown have
made a lot of very good Wine, and we are sending some
of it to another Cistercian Monastery because their
grapes did not do well this year. They had a drought or
something. I want you to go in the ship with the load of
wine and take it to the other Monastery."

"Yes, Father Abbot," said Walter in a Pleased voice.
He thought it would make a nice change. But in the
middle of the night in the Ship there was a Fierce Storm,
and all the sailors were in a terrible fright, and they went
to Walter and woke him up and asked him to pray for
them. "Because," they said, "you are a monk, and God

might, perhaps, listen to you more because you know Him better."

So Walter took his little Ivory Statue of Our Lady from under his pillow and he looked at it to gather his thoughts together and he said:

"Please, Our Lady, you have always been so kind to me, please will you ask God to remember us? I expect we are safe, really, but it is very Frightening for us to be in this Fierce Storm." And he went to sleep again, and while he was asleep God sent him a Dream, and this was the dream:

He thought that he saw a friend of his, called Brother Arnold, who was a monk at the Monastery, and who played the Harp. And Arnold was harping on his Harp and singing the Psalm about "Those who go down to the Sea in Ships."

Then Walter woke up, and he was very pleased, and he went to the sailors and said:

"It is all right. We won't be drowned, because my friend Arnold is harping on his Harp, and praying for us." And all the sailors cheered, and they sailed the ship safely into the harbour.

When Walter got back home he told the Abbot about his dream, and the Abbot sent for Arnold.

"Good morning, Brother Arnold," he said.

"Good morning, Father Abbot," said Arnold.

"What were you doing on Tuesday night?" said the Abbot.

"I couldn't go to sleep, and so I was praying for my friend, Brother Walter," said Arnold.

"But you were harping on your Harp," said the Abbot, "and you mustn't do that in the middle of the night. You might wake all the Others."

"But I don't *really* play my Harp, Father Abbot," said

Arnold. "I just pretend to play it with my fingers in the Dark, and I listen to the Imaginary Music."

So Walter thanked Our Lady very much for letting him hear Arnold's Imaginary Music, too, because it did cheer the sailors up wonderfully, and helped them to Weather the Storm.

A lot of other things happened to Walter (one was about two little French boys), but you will read about them all one of these days.

St. Walter's Special Day is on January 22nd, and there are many people called after him, but mostly Dutch people are, because he lived in Holland.

ST. HUMPHREY

ONCE upon a time there was an Abbot in Egypt, and his name was *not* Humphrey. One day this Abbot thought that he would like to go and see how all the Hermits in the Desert were getting on, and so he set out after dinner for a few days' Travel Round.

He visited first one and then another, and then he found a dead Hermit and buried him, and he spent the night in the dead Hermit's Cell, which was very Convenient. The next day he went Further into the Desert, and at last he came to a Cave. He peered inside. No one there! He went in and looked round carefully, because of robbers. It looked clean and swept, and there was a plant in a pot growing near the door. The Abbot felt the ashes of the fire, and they were Warm, and then he saw a plate and a jug of water.

"Someone lives here!" he said to himself. "And whoever it is can't be far away. I'll wait until he comes back."

So he sat on a stone just inside the door, and began to say his Office (which is prayers that priests say every day).

Soon he heard trampling, and cows mooing and a dog barking, and he looked out, and there was a man dressed like a monk coming along, driving some cows, with his dog running behind him.

When he got to the Cave the man stood Stock Still with Surprise!

"Who are you?" he asked. "I haven't seen a stranger for years and years!"

"I'm just an Abbot, doing some Visiting," said the Abbot. "Is there anything that I can do for you?"

"I am very Happy," said the Hermit. "God is very good to me."

"If I may say so," said the Abbot, "you are a funny sort of Hermit, having Pot Plants and Animals and things."

"Well," said the Hermit, whose name was *not* Humphrey, "I have them because God made them, and when

. . . you are a funny sort of Hermit.

I look at them I think how beautifully they are made. Sometimes things are even more beautiful inside than outside, and they are so neatly Fastened Off and Lined and all that. And if they are so Wonderful, then God who made them must be much more Wonderful. And if they are beautiful, then God who made them must be much more Beautiful. So that all the things that I see about me make me think of the Glory of God. Even Air."

"Why air?" asked the Abbot, in an Interested voice.

"Well, air is soft and invisible, and it doesn't look like anything, or feel like anything. It is so soft you can't feel it at all. *But* if I push a Tree I can't move it; God can move it about with Air. He can even blow it right over! And He doesn't have any sort of Machine to make the wind, like we would have to have. He just uses what's there."

"*Well*, now!" said the Abbot, "I never thought of that myself. What about the cows?"

The Hermit looked at the cows. "They wandered in here one night," he said. "I expect that God sent them in out of the cold. In return for that I look after them, and in return for that they give me milk. I give the milk to other Hermits, so that they can drink it and live to love and praise God. It all comes from God, and it all goes back to Him."

"I like your sort of Hermit," said the Abbot. "How do you manage for the Sacraments?"

"One of the nearby Hermits is a Priest," said the Hermit, "and we go to him on Sundays and holydays, and he says Mass."

"Good!" said the Abbot. "Well, I must be getting along. Good-bye, and God bless you!"

And he went off further and further into the Desert. After going along for seventeen more days he saw a man with long Hair and a Beard and dressed in a Rag.

"Oh, dear!" said the Abbot, "now this really *is* a Robber!" And he hid behind a rock and waited for the Man dressed in a Rag to pass by. But as he came up to the rock he said:

"Come out! my Lord Abbot. Don't be afraid of me, because I am here for the love of God."

"Well, now," said the Abbot. "I never would have

thought it, I'm sure." And he came out and Stared politely at the Man.

"Who are you, please?" he asked.

"I am a Hermit, and my name is Humphrey," said the man. "Would you like to come and spend the night with me?"

"Thank you," said the Abbot. "I am pretty tired."

Humphrey lived in a Cell under a Palm tree, which had dates growing on it. When they got there they found that it was so small that one of them would have to sleep outside, because there was not enough room for two. They decided that it would be more polite if they both slept out, and they did, and they had Dates for supper, and then they talked and talked.

"The last Hermit I visited," said the Abbot, "wasn't a *bit* the same as you. He had plants and things because they made him think more about God. You don't seem to have anything at all."

"I haven't got much," said Humphrey. "I eat what I find, mostly dates; and I drink water from the little well over there."

"But you haven't even got a cup or a plate or a bed!" said the Abbot.

"I have got a Cell for the winter, and when it rains," said Humphrey. "God is very good to me."

"That is what the other Hermit said," said the Abbot, "but why are you so *very* poor?"

"Well, Our Lord was very poor," said Humphrey.

"But not so poor as that," said the Abbot.

"No, but I am so much less Important than Our Lord," said Humphrey, "so it seems to me that I ought to be poorer and have less things. Also, if you haven't got anything you can't lose anything, and Robbers never come. If I have things then I have to look after them and think

about them sometimes, and that makes me have less time
to think about God."

"Well, now!" said the Abbot, "I never thought about
that myself. How do you manage about the Sacraments,
all these miles out in the Desert?"

"As a matter of fact," said Humphrey, looking Rather
Embarrassed, "an Angel brings me Holy Communion
every Sunday. My Guardian Angel it is."

"Does he *really*?" said the Abbot, all Astonished.
"God must love you very much."

"I love God very much," said Humphrey, "but I
shouldn't think that He has much reason to love
me."

"Shouldn't you?" said the Abbot, and they went to
sleep.

When the Abbot woke up in the morning he thought
that Humphrey looked Very Ill Indeed, and he said so.

"I know," said Humphrey, "I am going to die to-day,
and God sent you here so that you could hear my Confession and then Bury me."

The Abbot got the breakfast ready (it was dates and
water), and he went and sat sadly beside Humphrey.
He hadn't known him very long, but he liked him very
much, and he rather thought that he would like to be a
Hermit who had Nothing at All for the love of God.

Then Humphrey said:

"I'll tell you something, my Lord Abbot. After I die
and I am with God, if anyone remembers me and says a
prayer for me, or gives food to the Poor for me, I will
ask God to bless him. Our Lord told me that He would
do anything that I asked Him, once I had finished my
life here."

"Supposing that a man is too poor himself to give food
to a Beggar," said the Abbot, "won't you pray for him?"

"Well, if he burns some Incense and prays for me, that will be enough," said Humphrey.

"But supposing he is too poor even to get any Incense," said the Abbot, "won't you pray for him?"

"Well, he can just remember me and pray for me," said Humphrey, "and I will pray for him."

The Abbot gave him a very short Penance.

"I do wish," said the Abbot, "that I could stay here in your place when you have gone."

"No," said Humphrey, "you must go and tell the others about praying for me, so that I can pray for them."

And then he made his Confession, and the Abbot gave him a very short Penance because he was so Ill. And when he had said his Penance Humphrey left his poor

old body behind like an old coat and he went to God.
And the Abbot buried his body near the Palm Tree with
dates on it, and he thought that he would stay and be a
Hermit in Spite of what Humphrey had said. But just
as he had Decided the Palm Tree with dates on it
drooped and died, and fell on the Cell and flattened it
out!

Which did show that God wanted the Abbot to go back
and tell the others. If he hadn't gone back we would
never have known about Humphrey, would we?

St. Humphrey's Special Day is on June 12th, and it
is quite true that if people remember him in their prayers he will ask God to bless them. I think that lots of
people called Humphrey have never even heard of Saint
Humphrey, which is very Sad. But perhaps I am wrong.

ST. STEPHEN

ONCE upon a time there was a man called Stephen, and he was the Pope. Once upon the same time there was an Emperor called Valerian. (I don't know whether Valerian was called after the flower or the flower was called after Valerian, but it doesn't really matter, and anyway I always call the flower Kiss-me-quick.)

Valerian wanted to have a War with someone, because he had been training his soldiers for years, and they were quite Excellent, and it seemed such a Waste not to use them. But try how he would he couldn't find anyone who would fight with him, and he was in Despair! You remember that Pagans, like Valerian was, said that there were lots of Gods? Can you Imagine? They had a God of the Sun called Apollo and a Goddess of the Moon called Diana, and a God who made Thunderbolts and things called Vulcan, and a God of War called Mars. Well, Valerian and his Minions had been praying and praying to their God of War called Mars and burning Incense for him so that he would find them someone to fight with. But nothing happened, and you know why, don't you? Yes, because there is only one God, and there isn't such a person as Mars. It was rather like knocking and *knocking* on a door and waiting and *waiting* for someone to open it, and it is so sad for you because there is no one there, but you don't know that, and so you go on knocking.

At last one of the Minions said:

"What about that old Stephen who calls himself a Pope? The Christians say that if he prays to their God he often has his prayers answered."

"I don't Hold with Christians," said Valerian, "and I've been meaning to capture Stephen and his people for simply Ages."

"Well," said the Head Minion, "supposing we catch him and make him pray to Mars for us. If Mars still doesn't answer we can Kill Off old Stephen." (You do remember that Stephen was the Pope, don't you?)

"What an excellent Plan!" said Valerian, all Pleased. "Whoever captures Stephen can have his house and all his things. And whoever captures any of his friends can have any of their things!"

The next day the Minions started looking for Stephen because he was the most Important Christian, and they found him writing in his study.

"Come along, Stephen!" they said rudely. "You've got to come with us."

"Why?" asked Stephen, looking up from his writing.

"Because Mars won't listen to us, and Valerian wants you to come because you are good at Praying."

"Not to Mars, I'm not," said Stephen. And he picked up his pen again.

"Now then!" said the Top Minion; "orders is orders, and the Emperor Valerian's orders are that you are to go to him."

"Oh," said Stephen, "you didn't say that before." And because the Emperor was the most Important Person in the Land, and to avoid trouble, Stephen went with the Minions Quietly so as not to make an agitation among the Christians.

When they got to Valerian they found that he was waiting for them in the Temple of Mars, and crowds of Pagans had come to see the Pope of the Christians praying to the God of War.

Valerian explained to Stephen what it was he wanted.

"You must ask Mars to make people want to fight us," he said; "we want a War."

He knew that he was sure to be Killed anyway, because Valerian didn't hold with Christians, but he loved Our Lord very much, and he couldn't possibly pray to a False God.

"Go on!" said Valerian. "We are all waiting!" And the Minions who were holding Stephen pushed him down until he was kneeling in front of the Statue of Mars, and the people laughed to see the Pope of the Christians kneeling to one of their Gods.

Stephen made the Sign of the Cross and began to pray:

"Please, dear God," he said, "you see what is happening to me, and I am sorry I am kneeling in front of Mars, but I can't help it. *Please* could you do something to show these people that you are the only real living God, and that Mars is only a False God? I would not trouble you, only there is nothing that I can do myself alone."

And God listened to Stephen, and what do you think he did?

All of a sudden there was a great Cracking and Tearing and Rumbling noise, and all the people looked up just in time to see the roof fall in and the heaviest piece fell right onto the Statue of Mars and squashed it into little crumbs! Most of the people were killed, but not Valerian or Stephen.

Stephen got up and brushed the dust off his clothes and walked home. All the way he was thanking God for His wonderful help. "And surely," he said, "that must show the Pagans who is the Real God."

Next day was Sunday, and all the Christians, of course, went to Mass, but they hadn't got proper Churches because of Valerian and his Minions, and they used to have their Churches down in the Catacombs. (Do you remem-

ber the story of St. Philomena?) In case you don't, the
Catacombs were big underground caves and passages,
and the Christians used to have their churches and
chapels down there and their Baptisms and their Mar-
riages, and they were buried there, and sometimes they
even lived there. And because it was underground and
Dark they used a lot of candles, especially on the Altar,
so that the priest could see what he was reading. And
that is why we have Candles on our Altars, even in the
bright daylight, to remind us how much luckier we are
than the Early Christians.

Stephen had just got up to the Sermon, and he was
telling the people about Baptism when in came Valerian's Minions!

"What do you mean by walking off like that?" they
cried. "First you Ruin our temple, and then you make
us look for you all over again! Come along at once!"

"I can't," said Stephen. "I am in the middle of Mass."

"*We* don't mind," said one of the Minions.

"But God does, and so do I, and so do all the people
who have come to Mass," said Stephen, "and so I am
afraid that you will have to Wait."

Now when Stephen mentioned God the Minions felt
a bit nervous. They remembered what had happened
to Mars, and so they stood rather Grumpily at the back
of the Cave, and they watched Stephen go on with Mass
and give the people Holy Communion and then finish.

"I say," whispered one of the Minions, "I think that
there might be something in what all these people believe. It looks as if they really love their God."

"Stephen isn't a bad old man, really," said one of the
other Minions. "It is a pity that Valerian hates the Christians."

"We will have to kill him, whatever we think," said the first Minion. "Valerian is sure to Torture him, after yesterday."

"I know what," said one of the Minions. "Let's kill him here; it would be nicer for him, and then we can leave his body for his people to bury." And that is what they decided to do. So when Mass was finished the Head Minion went up to Stephen.

"I am sorry, Sir," he said, "that we interrupted your Mass, but we really do have to kill you because Valerian is our Emperor and he says so."

"Oh, yes," said Stephen, "I quite see that."

"But we thought," said the Minion, "that perhaps we could kill you here and now, with your own people, so that you needn't go back to Valerian."

"How kind of you!" said Stephen. "May I just go to Confession first?"

"Anything you like," said the Minions, and they waited while Stephen went to Confession. When he was ready he went and sat on his Pope's Throne and the Minions came very Politely and cut off his head, and all the people cried. But Stephen went straight to God and thanked Him very much indeed for letting him die so quickly and easily.

"Well," said God, "you are a good old man, Stephen, and you were really very Brave what with one thing and another. Do you know that those Minions are going to be Christians because they stayed to Mass?"

"*Are* they?" said Stephen. "*Well* now!"

St. Stephen's Special Day is on August 2nd. And although he is not by any means the only St. Stephen, I thought that I'd tell you about him because most books are about one of the others. Is your Birthday on August 2nd?

ST. ALICE

ONCE upon a time there was a Princess called Alice, and she had a Royal but Disreputable Family. (Disreputable is Dissipated in Appearance and Character.)

When she was sixteen Years old she married the King of Italy, and so she was the Queen of Italy, and she lived in Rome most of the time, and she often saw the Pope. But after only three years her husband, the King, died, and she was a Widow.

Now Alice had an Uncle Berengar, and he said to Alice:

"Now, my dear, I have a Plan for your future. You can't be a Widow when you are only Nineteen. You must marry my son Prince Adalbert."

"But," said Queen Alice, "I can't marry my Cousin! It isn't allowed, and besides, I don't like him!"

"Nonsense, girl!" said Alice's Uncle Berengar. "No one hereabouts knows that he is your Cousin, so what's the Odds?"

"But God will know," said Alice. "And, after all, it's God's rule that Cousins mustn't marry."

"Stuff!" said Alice's Uncle Berengar. "You *must* marry him, because I want him to be the King of Italy!"

But Alice wouldn't, and then Uncle Berengar showed himself in his True Colours. He sent for Alice's Ladies-in-Waiting and told them to take away her Jewels and her Costly Raiment and her shoes and even to cut off her Hair! Then she had a Sacking frock, and she was put in a Deep Dark dungeon under a castle on Lake Como.

But Alice had a lot of friends, and one of them was her old Palace Priest called Father John. When Father John heard what had happened to the Queen he was in a Great State.

"Poor girl!" he said. "I mean poor Her Majesty! I *must* go and see what I can do for the child; I mean for Queen Alice."

So he went to the castle by the lake and he looked at it carefully all the way round. Soon he saw a little Grating in the ground, and he peered in.

"Oh, Father John!" said a voice, "dear Father John, can you *possibly* get me out of this horrible place; it's got Black Beetles in it!"

"Well, my dear child, I mean Your Majesty," said old Father John, "I'll do what I can, but it won't be Too Easy, because I shall have to dig a Tunnel from a long way off and come up through your floor."

"Can I help?" asked Alice, a bit more cheerfully.

"Not with the Tunnelling," said Father John, "because someone might see you. But you must pray for me all the time, and then no one will catch me at it."

So Alice asked God if He would *please* not let anyone see Father John tunnelling. "Because I *do* want to get out of this Horrible place," she said to God. "But if you *want* me to stay here of course I will, and I won't even Mention the Black Beetles, even though they do give me the Cold Horrors." And often and often in the day she asked God the same thing, and whenever she woke up in the night she reminded Him, and she asked Our Lady to pray for Father John, too, and she did.

So every day old Father John tunnelled and tunnelled until he got right under Alice's floor, and then he began to tunnel upwards under Alice's floor, and sometimes Alice could hear Scratching and Bumping noises underneath. One day, under one of the stones of the floor came "Knock! Knock!" And Alice stared at the stone and very slowly it lifted up at the corner and there was Father John's round blue eye looking at her! She quickly lifted off the stone and Father John came out very Dusty and Cobwebby. He mopped his face with his handkerchief.

"Well, my dear, I mean Your Majesty," he said, "now how about getting out of this Ghastly Hole?"

"I would like to go now, really," said Alice. "It will soon be Dark."

So Alice popped down the hole, and they pulled the stone over the place (it made rather a scraping noise), and they hurried away down the tunnel. But an Unlucky thing happened.

The Dungeon Keeper just happened to be passing the door when he heard a Scraping Noise, and he stopped.

"I wonder what that Queen Alice is up to in there?" he said to himself, and he opened the door with his Jangling Key and looked inside. No Alice!

"Well!" said the Dungeon Keeper, "well, I *say!* Goodness me!" and he looked about, and he saw the loose stone. He shouted for the other Dungeon Keepers, and they all came, and they got down into the Tunnel and hurried after Alice and Father John!

After a few minutes Alice and Father John came out of the end of the tunnel into a cornfield, and they could hear the Dungeon Keepers coming after them, shouting and Jangling their Keys.

"Now, m'dear, I mean Your Majesty," said Father John, "I will go on along the path and the Dungeon Keepers will follow me. You stay among the corn, and they will pass you. If they catch me I'll say I'm just going for a walk or something!"

So he went off down the path beside the cornfield, and Alice popped into the tall corn and stood as still as a mouse! She'd only just got settled when the Dungeon Keepers rushed out of the end of the tunnel, shouting and Jangling their Keys, and they ran down the path after Father John.

Alice carefully peered about. No one to be seen! So she quietly went across the cornfield towards a town called Canossa, where there was a Fort. The Commander of the Fort was a man called Atto, and he was a very good friend of Queen Alice's, and she thought that perhaps she could stay with him until her luck changed. But Canossa (the town where the Fort was) was a long way off, and it was getting very Dark and Alice kept on walking and walking, and the ground got wetter and wetter, until she had no Idea where she was, and she was Lost! She thought that she had better keep on walking because (although she was not) the farther she walked the farther she would be from the Dungeon by the lake!

But when it was Quite Dark a Terrible Thing happened! Suddenly the ground got much softer and wetter, and Alice's foot went Right In. Then her other foot went in past her knee, and she couldn't get it out! Alice was so frightened that she just stood quite still without moving, and she sank deeper and deeper, until both her legs were Right In.

"I'm in a Marsh!" she said to herself. "What *shall* I do? By the time it is the morning I shall have sunk so far that it will be past my Head and I shall be Drowned in Mud!"

The mud was very cold and clammy, and when Alice tried to move her feet it made horrible loud Sucking noises, and Frogs and things came plopping about

frightening Alice out of her Wits. (Your Wits are your
natural Intelligence, or the Sense you were Born With.
Do you know the story of Epaminondas who hadn't got
the Sense he was Born with?)

After a long time Alice was as deep as her Middle,
and she was freezing cold. But still she hadn't thought of
what to do. I expect that by now you will have thought
of her Guardian Angel, haven't you? But poor Alice,
having Lost her Wits, never thought of anything at all.

Then God, who is always so Kind, was sorry for Alice,
and He put a thought into her head and this was the
thought:

"*What* about my Guardian Angel? Why didn't I think
of him before? I must have lost my Wits!" And she said
to her Guardian Angel:

"Please, my Good Angel, whom God has appointed
to be my Guardian, watch over me during this night! I
am so sorry that I forgot you, but I was in such a Fright
that I couldn't think of anything at all."

And then she waited and waited for her Guardian
Angel to help her. You see, however good a person is
(and after all Alice was a Saint), they can't do *anything
at all* without God. So Alice couldn't even think of her
Guardian Angel until God gave her the thought. Did
you know that if God stopped thinking about you for
One Second you wouldn't be there at all? Neither would
the trees in the garden, or your dog, or anything that is
alive, because God is Life as well as Everything else.

After some time Alice saw a little Little light moving
about, and it came nearer and nearer, and went this
way and that, until she began to hear little Splashing
noises and Bumping noises, and then she heard a cough!

"Hello!" she shouted. "Please come this way, whoever you are! I am stuck in a Marsh!"

The light came nearer and nearer, and there was a Fisherman in a Boat!

"Whatever are you doing there, Miss?" he said in a Surprised voice. "You'll get your Death of Cold!"

And he pulled Alice out, all covered with slippery Mud, and got her into the boat.

The Fisherman's wife put Alice to bed.

"Lucky for you that I came this way, Miss," he said, and he covered Alice up with some nets, which was better than nothing. "I only come this way Tuesdays as a rule, and it's Friday to-day. I really don't know what made me alter my mind."

"It was my Guardian Angel," said Alice. "He was Watching Over me during the Night." And she rubbed off some of the mud with a piece of Fishing Net.

"Well, I never saw anything of him, if he did, Miss," said the Fisherman. "But it was very kind of him, I'm sure."

So Alice went home with the Fisherman, and the Fisherman's wife dried Alice and washed her clothes and put her to bed with a bowl of Hot Bread and Milk to keep out the cold. In the morning she *was* surprised to see that the poor muddy girl called Alice was really Queen Alice! She talked about it for years and years afterwards.

So many other things happened to Alice that there wouldn't be room in the book for anyone else if I told you any more. But when she got married again she had a Son, and when he grew up he married a Greek Princess who was Incredibly Beautiful, and who had a Feathered Harness for her horse and had hundreds of Jewels and Pearls, and wore her hair in a Golden Net. But she wasn't very nice to Alice, I must say.

Alice's Special Day is on December 16th, and anyone whose Birthday is on that day can have her for their Special Saint, but specially someone that I know whose name is Alice Mary.

ST. JENNIFER

ONCE upon a time there was a little girl and her name was Jennifer, and she lived near Paris with her Mother and her Father, who was a shepherd, and she was seven years old.

One day the Pope said to his Secretary:

"You know, those Pelagian people in Britain are becoming a Perfect Nuisance." (Do you remember the Pelagians that St. David argued with? They were the people who said: Everything you *can't* do you *needn't* do!)

The Pope's Secretary waited to see what the Pope was Getting At.

"We must send one of our Bishops over to Britain," said the Pope, "and we will see if he can get some Sense into their heads. I thought Bishop Germain would be a good man."

So the Secretary wrote to Germain, and he started the very next week, and on his way to Britain he had to go through Paris and stay the night there. (Now you know why I am telling you all this!)

When the people in Paris heard that the Bishop was coming and that he would say Mass in the morning, they all got up early and went to Church to hear what he had to say. But instead of a Sermon he said:

"I want you all to come to me one at a time and I will Bless you all." And they did, and when it was Jennifer's turn the Bishop blessed her and then he said:

"Whose little girl is this?" and the people said:

"She belongs to the shepherd, and her name is Jennifer."

"Well, Jennifer," said the Bishop, "so you are going
to live for God, are you?"

"Yes, Father," whispered Jennifer. She was very
Shy, because the Bishop was talking to her with all the
other people Staring.

"Good," said the Bishop, and then he bent down and
picked up a little piece of money with a cross on it
(somebody must have dropped their Collection), and
he gave it to Jennifer and he said:

"Keep this to remind you to live for God, and never
miss Mass on Sundays or Holidays. Ask someone to make
a little hole in it and wear it round your neck like a
Medal." Then Jennifer went away to make room for
the next person.

After that Jennifer always wore her little bit of money,
even when she was grown up.

One day it was Ascension Day, and her mother was
getting ready to go to Mass, but she didn't say anything
about Jennifer going.

"Please may I go and get ready, too?" asked Jennifer.

"You aren't going," said her Mother, and she began
looking for her coat.

"*Please*, Mummy," said Jennifer. "The Bishop did
say that I must, and I do want to, because of living for
God."

Jennifer's mother was Angry.

"Do as you are told!" she said. "Holidays of Obliga-
tion are for grown-ups and *not* for children. Now, that's
enough!"

"But . . . " Jennifer began to say, and her mother
came and slapped her on both cheeks very hard and
said:

"Be quiet! And now, to serve you right, I won't let
you go to Mass on Sundays either!"

Now nearly always people's mothers are Absolutely Right. But this time Jennifer's mother was Absolutely Wrong, which is a Most Unusual Thing. God didn't like the way she was behaving, and He didn't want Jennifer to miss Mass on Sundays. Besides, He wanted Jennifer to be one of His Special People when she grew up. So to serve her mother right He made her Blind in both Eyes!

"Oh dear, oh dear, Jennifer," she said. "I can't see! You must have drawn the curtains, you naughty girl! Draw them back at once!"

"But the room is all sunny!" said Jennifer; "it isn't dark at all!"

Her mother stayed blind for more than a year, and all the time she wouldn't let Jennifer go to Mass at all. At last she said to herself:

"I must be Blind because I never let Jennifer go to Mass. God must have done it to show me." And she began to pray, and to tell God how sorry she was that she had been so Stupid. Just then Jennifer came in with a jug of water to fill the kettle.

"Come here, Jennifer," said her mother, "dip your finger in the water and make the Sign of the Cross on my eyelids."

And Jennifer did, and her mother could see a little, and in three days she was quite well again, and after that she always took Jennifer to Church with her.

When she grew up Jennifer was a Nun, and she lived in Paris. She was very good at Massage (which is Rubbing a thing Better), and she used to carry a little bottle of Oil in her pocket so that she could Rub anyone who needed it.

"God must have blessed my Hands," she used to say, "because He so often uses them to make people better."

One Sunday a man with a Lame Hand came to her. He couldn't move it at all.

"How did it get like that?" said Jennifer.

"It came like that when I was a little boy," said the man.

Jennifer felt in her pocket for her little bottle of Oil, but when she got it out it was empty!

"Oh, *dear!*" she said, "the oil is finished! I am afraid that I will hurt you if I do it with nothing. Could you come to-morrow and I'll buy some more oil. I can't to-day because it is Sunday."

But the man couldn't see her the next day (I don't know why), so Jennifer said to God:

"Please what shall I do, because there is no oil? The poor man has a very bad Lame Hand, dear Lord, please help me to make it better."

Then she picked up her bottle to put it back in her pocket, and she saw that it was full of oil! It had a lovely Sweet Smell, and it lasted her for years.

So Jennifer took hold of the man's hand, and she moved it and she rubbed it with the oil, and she bent his fingers and she pulled them, and all that, and when she had finished it was Quite Cured, and he was so pleased that he sent her six Eggs and some Lettuces for a present.

Once Attila, the King of the Huns, was fighting in France, and he got nearer and nearer to Paris because he wanted to Capture it. The people in Paris were in a Great Way. The men all got their weapons and their helmets out and put food and things in their pockets, and went out to fight him, and all the women began Packing their Things.

"Why are you all Packing your Things?" asked Jennifer in a surprised voice.

"Because Attila is coming, and we want to save our Goods and Chattels," said the women.

"Are you going to be Refugees, all along the roads?" asked Jennifer.

"Yes," said the women. "There's nothing else to do."

"Well," said Jennifer, "it would be much more Sensible not to Clutter up the roads for the soldiers. Why don't you all come with me to the Church and pray that Attila won't come? With God on our side it will be much better staying here than being Refugees."

Some of the women said that she was quite right, but some of them said that she was a wicked Spy on Attila's side. In the end they nearly all went to the Church, and Jennifer prayed, and they all prayed, and when they came out of the Church they met all the soldiers coming home.

"But what about Attila?" asked all the women.

"Well," said one of the soldiers, "it is a very Funny Thing, but a little while ago Attila and all his Huns turned round and marched away!" And so Paris was saved; and Jennifer's idea about the women was a good one, wasn't it?

Jennifer's favourite Saint was St. Denis, and she very much wanted to have a Church in Paris called after him. So she asked some priests if it could be built. But they said that no one could ever build anything ever again because people had forgotten how to make the lime for the mortar to stick the bricks together.

"The Romans used to make it when they were here," said the priests, "but that was ages ago, and we haven't any lime Kilns." (Kilns are places where lime is made.)

"Well, you go and stand on the bridge in the middle of Paris," said Jennifer, "and you shall hear what you shall hear."

So the priests went and stood on the bridge, and felt a bit Awkward just standing there and doing nothing.

Soon two Swineherds (which are people who look after Pigs like Shepherds look after Sheep) came walking along, and as they passed the priests one Swineherd said to the other:

"Yesterday one of my Pigs ran into the Forest, and when I found it, it was by an Enormous Lime Kiln full of Lime. It must have been left there by the Romans."

"What a funny thing!" said the other Swineherd. "Because I saw a blown-down tree the other day in the Forest, and at its roots there was a big Lime Kiln full of Lime! Isn't that an Extraordinary Coincidence!" (A Coincidence is when two things happen at the same time.)

The priests were Delighted. They ran after the swineherds and found out where the lime kilns were, and there was plenty of lime for the Church of St. Denis, and it was built at once.

One of these days you must read a book about St. Jennifer because so many things happened to her that I have only had time to tell you one or two of them.

St. Jennifer's Special Day is on January 3rd, and she is the Special Saint for Paris. Anyone called Geneviève can have her for their Saint, because Geneviève is the French for Jennifer.

ST. MUNGO

ONCE upon a time there was a Monastery at Culross, in Fifeshire, in Scotland, and it was a Boys' School, and it was near the sea.

Very early one morning one of the monks (whose name was Servan) was saying his Office when God said to him:

"Servan, go down to the sea and you will find something."

So Servan got up and put his Breviary away, and then he went outside. It was so very early in the morning that it was still nearly dark, but he found the path that led to the sea, and was soon on the Beach. There he saw a Dark Bundle. He peered at it, and found that it was a Girl wrapped up in a dark cloak with a tiny, brand-new Baby! They were sopping wet, and the girl was Very Ill with a Temperature.

"Poor things!" thought kind old Brother Servan, "they must have been wrecked or something!" and he lifted up the girl and her baby and carried them back to the Monastery. He called the other Monks, and they gave the girl a Hot Tot to try and warm her up, but it was so sad because she soon died. She had caught her Death of Cold.

So there were the Monks in the Abbey at Culross with a tiny little boy of one day old in their School!

They Baptised him Kentigern, but he was such a nice baby that everybody called him Mungo, which means Dearest.

When Mungo was old enough he went to the school

He started to say the Prayer to the Holy Spirit.

with the other boys, but they didn't like him because he belonged to the Monks, and the Abbey was his home.

"That Mungo gets all the Tit Bits when we're not looking," they said, "and I expect he Tells Tales about us to Brother Servan." Mungo didn't do any of those things, but the Other Boys used to do everything that they could to make his life Miserable.

There were no matches in those days, and so the Kitchen Fire had to be kept burning Day In and Day Out, because it was such a bother to relight it. So it was the job of the boys to take it in turns to get up in the Middle of the Night to make up the fire. Once, when it was Mungo's turn to get up, he found that the Other Boys had poured some water on it, and that it was dead out. Poor Mungo was Distracted! He wasn't quite sure how to light it again (one of the monks always did it), and if he left it then none of them would be able to have any Breakfast! Now whenever anything happened Mungo used to tell the Holy Spirit, and so, before he thought what he was doing he started to say the Prayer to the Holy Spirit to comfort himself. And what do you suppose happened? When he got to "Enkindle in them the Fire of thy love," all the dead wet ashes blazed up, and there was a lovely Hot Fire! When the Other Boys came down in the morning they were all whispering and Nudging one another while they were waiting for Breakfast. "Now," they said to each other, "that horrid little Mungo will get into trouble, because there won't *be* any Breakfast!"

But when the servery door opened, instead of an Angry Brother Cook, there was their nice Hot Breakfast just the same as usual! So they thought of a worse thing to do and this was the Worse Thing.

Old Brother Servan had a tame Robin that used to

come into his room and pick up crumbs and sit on the
back of his chair and all that. (I expect that you have
often seen Robins in the house. There is one that nearly
lives in my Kitchen!) Servan was very fond of his Robin,
and he was always hoping that one day it would get
tame enough to sit on his finger, but it hadn't yet.

One day, while Brother Servan was teaching in the
school, some of the boys caught the Robin and killed
it and put it in Mungo's pocket with a few feathers stick-
ing out so that it would show. They put the coat in
Servan's room so that when he came in and saw the
coat he would think that it was Mungo who had done it.
But luckily it was Mungo who came in first, and he saw
the Robin.

"Oh, *poor* little thing!" said Mungo. "What a *shame*!
What will poor old Brother Servan do when he knows?"
And he began to cry, it was so sad. And he began to say
his favourite Prayer to the Holy Spirit. While he was
saying, "they shall be Created," the Robin shook out its
crumpled little feathers and flew to Brother Servan's
desk! There it sat, tidying itself up, and Mungo couldn't
thank God enough for saving Brother Servan from being
so sad.

But at last Mungo was so Miserable because of the
Other Boys that he ran away! Brother Servan followed
him.

"Now, Mungo," he said, "never you mind those silly
boys! We all know that you are all right, and that you
don't do all these Fearful Things," and he patted Mungo's shoulder kindly.

"I know, Brother," said Mungo sniffing sadly, and
rubbing his nose, "but I couldn't go back, really I
couldn't. Besides, I do want to be a Hermit for a little
while, and then I want to be a Priest."

"All right, then," said Servan, "but come and see us whenever you like; we shall always be pleased to see you."

"Yes, I will," said Mungo, "because you are all my Fathers, and the Abbey is my Home."

Mungo found a cave near Glasgow, on the banks of the Clyde, and he did just what he had said. First he was a Hermit, and then he was a Priest, and in time he was made the Bishop of Glasgow. He spent a lot of time teaching people about God, and once he went to Wales. (Do you remember when David had a Meeting and a lot of Bishops and things went to it? Well, Mungo was one of the Bishops.)

Now when Mungo was the Bishop of Glasgow the King's name was King Roderick, and they were great friends. King Roderick's wife was a Young and Giddy Queen, and once she did a very Young and Giddy thing. She gave her Engagement Ring, that King Roderick had given to her before they were married, to a Knight that she liked very much.

"You can wear it as a Favour," she said to him. (Have you read the story of St. Walter yet? If you have you will know what a Favour is.) And the Knight put it on his finger and thought that no one would notice.

One day King Roderick and the Knight went hunting together, and they got very hot and tired, so the King said:

"Let's stop and have our lunch under these trees by the stream. We can get cool, and we might have Forty Winks."

So they had a lovely Cold Lunch that the Queen had packed for them. They had Chicken Patties and New Bread and New Butter and Cheese and Wild Strawberries and Whisky. Then they put the plates and things

back in the basket and settled down for their Forty
Winks.

But King Roderick wasn't so sleepy as the Knight,
and he lay on his back and stared at the leaves against
the sky, and thought about his Young and Giddy Queen.
Then he rolled over and looked at the Knight who was
asleep, and there, on his finger, he saw the Queen's
Engagement Ring!

He was Simply Furious. He leaned over and very
carefully pulled off the ring without waking the Knight
and Threw it in the stream.

When they got home he asked the Young and Giddy
Queen where her Ring was. "You ought to wear it always with your Wedding Ring," he said.

"I've lost it," said the Queen, feeling Rather Nervous.

"Well, why did you take it off, then?" said King
Roderick.

"It must have Fallen Off," said the Queen. "I'm
thinner than I was," she said in a Pathetic voice.

"Then you must find it," said King Roderick in a
Stern voice. "If you don't find it by to-morrow lunch
time I shall know that you have been Giddier than usual
and you will have to be Executed. Queens can't afford
to be Giddy." And he Stamped out of the room.

The poor Queen was very Frightened, and she sent
a quick message to her Favourite Knight, and this was
the quick message:

"Send back my Ring Quickly, because if you don't
I will be Executed to-morrow at Lunch Time."

But the Knight sent back a quick message, and this
was his quick message:

"I can't, because it was lost when I was out hunting
with the King."

The Queen was in a Frenzy of Despair, and she sent

for the Bishop of Glasgow, who was Mungo, and she went to Confession, and told him all about everything. So Mungo gave her Absolution and a Penance, and he was sorry for her, because she was so Young and Giddy, and so he went to the Church and he prayed and prayed that she wouldn't have to be Executed.

"Because, dear Lord," he said to God, "she really is sorry she was so Silly, and it does seem a shame to Execute her when she is so Young."

When he got back to his Bishop's Palace in Glasgow, he found a Mysterious Parcel waiting for him. It was Long and Heavy and Rather Damp.

"Well now," said Mungo to himself, "who could be sending me a present at this time of night? I do believe it smells of Fish!"

And he unpacked his Parcel, and there inside it was a fresh-caught Salmon from the River Clyde!

"How very kind of Who-ever-it-is," said Mungo. "I'll invite some Poor-and-Raggy people to dinner to-morrow, and we'll have my Fine Fat Salmon!" And he took it to the kitchen.

Early in the morning, on his way back from Mass, his servant met him.

"Look, my Lord," he said. "Look what the cook found inside the Salmon!" And there was the Queen's ring!

Mungo quickly took it to the Queen, and when King Roderick went to see her after breakfast she said:

"Here is my Ring, Roderick. Will you please forgive me?"

And Roderick was so Surprised that he said that he would if she promised not to be so Giddy again. And she did.

Anybody who lives in Glasgow will know that in the crypt of the Cathedral is St. Mungo's Tomb (which is where he was buried when he died) and I expect lots of people have seen it. Have you?

St. Mungo's Special Day is on January 13th, but not many people out of Scotland are called after him. I really made this story for somebody called Cora, because she hasn't got a Special Saint, and so she is always called Mungo.

ST. OWEN

ONCE upon a time there was a Prime Minister whose name was Owen, and he was Prime Minister for Queen Audrey, who was a Royal Nun. Now Queen Audrey was having a Holiday from being a Nun, so that she could build an Abbey and Cathedral on the Island of Ely, which belonged to her, and while she was doing all that Owen did the Ruling in the Island.

Queen Audrey, as I expect you know, was building her Abbey and Cathedral on one of the Hard Places in the Fens that are called Islands, but they are not near the sea at all, and they are only Islands when the Floods come and make all the Soft Places into swamps and lakes and that sort of thing. Well, what with seeing to the Building and Draining her Island as much as she could she left more and more of her Governing work to Owen, and once every week or so he used to go and see her on Business or something.

One day he went to Ely to see the Queen on Matters of State, and found her choosing patterns for the Carving inside the Cathedral.

"Good morning, Your Majesty," said Owen, bowing Politely.

"Good morning, Prime Minister," said Queen Audrey, "which do you like best, This or That?"

"This, I think, Your Majesty," said Owen. "It looks more Dignified, don't you think?"

"I believe you are right," said Queen Audrey. "You usually are."

"Well, Your Majesty," said Owen, "I really came to

say that your People would like to see a bit more of you now that you are out of your Convent for a while, and they sent me to ask if you would go and do some Reigning for a little while."

"But I am just in the middle of building my Cathedral," said Queen Audrey. "I couldn't go now, possibly."

"Good morning, Your Majesty," said Owen.

"Perhaps I could stay and look after it for you," said Owen. "I could always ask you if I wasn't Sure."

So that is what they did, and Queen Audrey went back to her Palace, and all the people Cheered.

Now Prime Minister Owen got more and more Interested in the Cathedral, and soon he could think of nothing else.

"How much more Satisfactory," he thought to himself, "it is to work for God than it is to work for a Queen, however Good and Noble she may be; I *do* like building Cathedrals!"

As time went on he thought more and more about making the Cathedral more and more Beautiful because of God being the most Beautiful of All. (Beauty is one of the Divine Attributes, but you wouldn't know about that.)

"That is not beautiful enough," he would say to the Carving Men, or:

"Make it more beautiful than that," he would say to the Painting Men. At last the workmen began to get Irritated.

"We are making the most beautiful things that we have ever made," they said, "and you are not Satisfied. What is the matter with you?"

"What *is* the matter with me?" said the Prime Minister Owen to himself. "Nothing seems Perfect, and I want it to be Perfect as God Himself is Perfect."

He went into the Cathedral and stared at the lovely Carvings and things.

"Perfect," he said, "perfect. I know what I want! I want God, not His Cathedral! I'll go away and be a Monk and belong to God, who is the most Beautiful of All."

He called all the Workmen and said to them:

"Listen, everybody! I've just had a very Good Idea, and I want you to make a Stone Cross and put it just here where I had the Idea, to remind people of the Beauty of God. And I want it to be Perfectly Plain."

"What!" said the Head Carver. "No carving?"

"What!" said the Head Painter. "No painting?"

"No," said the Prime Minister Owen, "just a Plain Cross. If you carve it, it would be like carving Patterns on a Flower, and if you paint it, it would be like painting colours on a Butterfly. Just Plain, I want it."

So they made a Plain Stone Cross, and they put it where Owen had had his Good Idea, and then he went and told Queen Audrey that he was Leaving.

"But, my dear Prime Minister!" said Queen Audrey, "I can't run the Kingdom without you. But I must say, being a Monk is a Far, far Better Thing."

"You'll get along without me very well, Your Majesty," said Owen; "of course you will." And he went up to his room. He took off all his Rich and Rare Prime Minister's clothes and put on very Plain ones. Then he went out and got a Spade and an Axe from the potting shed and went to say Good-bye to the Queen.

"Why on Earth are you taking those with you?" asked Queen Audrey as she stood at the Front Door to see him off.

"It's part of my Idea. Good-bye, Your Majesty," said Owen, and he walked away down the drive, out the front gate and turned to the left down the long road.

He went to a Monastery at Lastingham, near Whitby, that he knew of, where the Abbot's name was Chad. (He was St. Chad, actually.) When he got there he knocked at the door and waited.

"Good evening!" said the Brother Porter as he opened the door, "what may I do for you?"

"May I please see the Abbot?" asked Owen.

"Please step this way," said the Brother Porter politely, and Owen, with his Axe and his Spade, followed him along the long stone passage until they came to a door. The Brother Porter knocked and someone said, "Come in!"

"Somebody to see you Father Abbot." And Owen went in.

"Good evening," said the Abbot, whose name was Chad, "what may I do for you?"

"Please may I be a Monk in your Monastery?" said Owen.

"Why?" said the Abbot whose name was Chad.

"Because the only thing that I *really* want is God."

"Well, that is as good a Beginning as any," said the Abbot whose name was Chad, "but why the Axe and the Spade, if you don't mind my asking?"

"Not at all," said Owen. "I brought them because I can't Sing in Tune, so I thought I could perhaps work with my Hands to the Glory of God instead of with my Voice."

"Well, that is as good a reason as any," said the Abbot whose name was Chad. "Would you mind being the Brother Gardener-who-also-looks-after-the-Chickens?"

"Thank you, Father Abbot," said Brother Owen, who wasn't a Prime Minister any more, "that is exactly what I should like to be!"

So Owen worked outside all day. He grew the most beautiful flowers he could for the Chapel, and when he took them to the Brother Sacristan who looked after the Altar he used to stop by the Blessed Sacrament and say to God:

"Here, dear Lord, are some of your flowers for you. I know that you made them yourself, but nothing that I could make would be so beautifully made as these. All I can do is to dig the soil and sow the seed and water it when it is dry and wait for you to make it grow."

He grew vegetables and fruit for the Monks to eat, and soon he knew all about Trenching and Double Digging and Pruning and Stopping and Mulching and all That.

He kept the Chickens and the Hens, and the Brothers all said that they had never had so many Eggs before, and how *did* Brother Owen manage it.

. . . there was Owen kneeling by his Crocuses.

One day all the Monks were in the Chapel singing Compline, and Owen was outside tying black Cotton round about the Crocuses to keep the Sparrows from spoiling them. The Abbot was in his study, and all of a sudden he heard the sound of singing very far away. He stopped reading and listened.

"It must be a Procession!" he thought. "I wonder where it can be coming from?"

He looked out of the window, but he could only see Owen cottoning his crocuses. The singing came nearer and nearer, until at last it was in the Abbot's study, but still he couldn't see anything! He listened to the singing, and got more and more interested in what he heard, so that before he could think about it, it was half an hour later, and the singing Procession was going away again. When it had gone the Abbot looked out of the window again, but all that he could see was Owen still kneeling by his crocuses and threading the cotton between them.

The Abbot clapped his hands, and Owen looked up.

"Come up here a minute, Brother Owen," said the Abbot.

Owen stood up and brushed his knees with his hands and rubbed his hands on his Sacking Apron.

"Certainly, Father Abbot," he said. And he went up to the Abbot's study.

"Did you hear anything, Brother Owen?" said the Abbot.

"No, Father Abbot," said Owen.

"Well, some people were singing," said the Abbot.

"I know," said Owen.

"How do you know?" asked the Abbot.

"I saw them," said Owen.

"Did you indeed?" said the Abbot, all Astonished. "Who were they?"

"Angels," said Owen.

"*Well!*" said the Abbot. "You saw them and I heard them, but I thought that they were in here."

"They were," said Owen. "The room was full of them. I saw them through the window. They passed me on their way in."

"They told me that I would die in Seven Days," said the Abbot. "It is very kind of them to let me know so that I shall have time to get ready to see God. They told me lots of other things, too, but I can't tell you, because they said that they were a Secret!" The Abbot whose name was Chad looked very Wise and Solemn. "Well, Brother Owen, aren't you Rather Sorry that I can't tell you the Secrets?"

"No, Father Abbot," said Owen.

"Why not?" said the Abbot. "After all anyone might reasonably feel a little Jealous if he wasn't allowed to hear a Secret like that."

"Because they *showed* me something," said Owen.

"*Did* they now?" said the Abbot, opening his eyes very wide. "What did they show you?"

"They said that was a Secret, too," said Owen, and bowing politely to the Abbot he went away. When the Abbot looked out of the window there he was, kneeling by his crocuses with a reel of Black Cotton in his hand and a look of Great Happiness on his face.

The Abbot did die in seven days, and he had plenty of time to put his affairs in order, but no one ever knew what it was that the Angels had shown to Owen.

St. Owen's Special Day is on March 4th, and there are a lot of people called after him. The Plain Stone Cross that he put in Queen Audrey's Cathedral at Ely is still there. Perhaps you will see it one day, and remember Owen's Good Idea.

ST. DAVID

ONCE upon a time there was a Welsh man and his name was David, and he lived in Wales, and he was very Good at Farming and Gardening and Fishing and all that. As time went on he used to look at the Mountains and the Rivers and he thought to himself:

"How Grand and Lovely all these things are, and how Clever of God to have thought of them. I have to carry water to water my plants, but God puts His plants in a Valley and makes the River run down the Mountain to water them, or else He makes it Rain on them. I have to put my plants in a greenhouse to keep them warm, but God makes the Sun shine on His."

And more and more he used to sit and stare at all the things of Nature, and think how Marvellous it all was!

"Fancy thinking of making little coloured feathered things that fly!" he thought; "and fancy making them sing and build nests!" And he listened to the birds singing, and thought how wonderful God was to Invent all these things.

At last David built himself a tiny little House with one room in it, and lived there all alone thinking and thinking about God. He would look at a Mountain and he would think this thought:

"How strong and big God is, like a Mountain. He never changes whatever happens, and He is always there."

And he would look at the River and he would think this thought:

"How clean and cool God is, and He is always ready

to run to help us; nothing will stop Him. He is like a River, and we live in Him and He is all round us like the little brown trout in the water."

And when it Rained he would think this thought:

"The Rain comes and Freshens the earth and waters the growing things and makes them live. God is like the

David peacefully thinking about God in Nature.

Rain, and He freshens our minds when we are Cross and Tired. We couldn't live without Him."

And in the Sunshine he thought:

"The Sun is warm and comforting and gives us light to see by. It is like the Warm and Comforting Love of God shining on everybody and everything that He has made."

And he thought like this of all Nature, like the Wind

and the Sky and the Green Grass and the Sea, until he suddenly had a Good Idea.

"I know!" he said. "We can't *see* God himself, but He lets all the things that He has made remind us of Him, and all these things must be Good because He made them."

And he was quite right, because you couldn't have a Bad Sweet Pea, now could you? Or a Wicked Rabbit, or a Jealous Cloud, or a Proud Hayfield, and an Angry Tree? It is only People who do these things—which is so Sad, because God made us, too. (Why did God Make us?)

So there was David in his little house peacefully thinking about God in Nature (like Owen thought of God being Beautifulness) and the more he thought about God the more he learned about Him.

Now there was another Welsh man called Morgan, and everyone called him Pelagius (I can't think why, because his name was Morgan, however), and he started out by being a very good and holy man, who used to teach a lot of people about God. But suddenly the Devil popped an Idea into his head, and instead of Morgan saying: "Go away, Devil! *I* know you and your Tricks; this is one of *your* Ideas and I won't think it," he said:

"Now that is an Excellent Idea, and I will teach it to all my people." So he started to teach the Devil's Idea to everybody along with teaching them all the True things. And this was the Devil's Idea:

Everything you ought to do you can do, and do it by yourself without the help of God.

But that is the same as saying:

Everything you can't do you needn't do.

And that was the part that the people liked. A Thief could say, "But I am always a Thief, I was made that way, and I *can't* be Honest. And if I can't be Honest then I needn't be!"

And a Bad Tempered person could say: "But I always have had a Bad Temper, I was born with it, I *can't* be Good Tempered. And if I can't be, then I needn't be!"

All the people thought that this Devil's Idea was a lovely one, because they could be as Bad as they liked and say that they couldn't help it. And more and more and more people all over the World used the Idea, especially in Wales, because of Morgan (who was called Pelagius) being a Welsh man. And the Devil was delighted because he was winning so many people away from God with his Idea. Another part of the Idea was that some of the things in Nature were Wicked, which is very Silly, because if God invented Wicked things, then He would be Wicked Himself, which is just Plain Stupid.

Well, things got so bad and people stopped going to Mass and they never went to Confession (because they said that it wasn't their Fault that they were Bad) and they didn't let their babies be Baptised because they said that there wasn't any Original Sin. At last all the Bishops and Princes and Abbots and things had a Meeting with all the Pelagians at a place in Wales called Brefi (St. Mungo was one of the Bishops who went there, from Glasgow). They argued and they argued, and first one side seemed to be winning and then the other, but they *couldn't* get it settled. At last one of them said:

"What about sending for David? He is a very Wise Hermit, and perhaps he could make these Pelagian People see sense."

So they sent two men called Daniel and Devereux to David's cell, and there was David making deep little holes and planting Leeks in his garden.

"But I don't want to go and do a lot of Arguing," said

David, when Daniel and Devereux had told him what they wanted. "It is nice and Peaceful here, and God is Good."

"But it isn't Peaceful there for all of us with those Pelagians all over the place," said Daniel; "they're turning Wales into a Perfect Bedlam! If you will come and if you happen to Win the Argument, then we can *all* be Peaceful, not only you!"

"Well," said David, and he planted the last leek of the row, "if you put it like that I suppose that I ought to go with you." So he put away his Trowel, and he shut his Front Door, and went away with Daniel and Devereux.

When they got to Brefi the Bishops and things were still Arguing, and the Pelagians were still Shouting, and everything was in a Pandemonium. (Which means that there were Devils all over the place, and perhaps there were.)

David stepped up onto a little knob of ground and clapped his hands and shouted "Hey!"

That made all the people stop talking and look at him, which was what he wanted, and he started telling the Pelagians, not how Stupid their devil's Idea was, but Why it was stupid. And because he knew such a lot about God he told them about Him, too. And because he wasn't Calling them Names but just Explaining, the people listened, and as they listened a Most Extraordinary thing happened.

The Knob of Ground where David was standing grew bigger and bigger, and taller and taller, until it turned into a High Hill, and his voice got louder and louder, so that in Spite of standing on the top of the High Hill the people could still hear him talking!

What with all that and David's most Excellent Speech,

the Pelagians stopped being so Tiresome and went to Church again. But of course there were still lots of them all over the World, and there are still a few about to this very day, and I expect you have seen some, but you didn't Know it!

The Bishops and Princes and Abbots and things were so pleased with David because God had done this Surprising thing for him, that they made him the Head Bishop in Wales. And the New High Hill that wasn't there before was called Llandevi Brefi (which means David's Hill at Brefi) and there it is still.

Now that David was an Important Bishop he started building Monasteries specially for Monks, who would teach all the Pelagians to be Christians again. He built Twelve, and the one that he lived in himself was at a place called Mynyw (or Menevia for people who can't Spell in Welsh).

All these Monks of David's Farmed and Gardened and all that as well as doing their Teaching, and they all kept Bees for Honey for the Ill people with Coughs.

One of the Monks who was a Brother Beekeeper was called Modemnoc, and the bees loved him, and they would never sting him, and they used to follow him about the garden.

One day David said to Modemnoc:

"Brother, I want you to sail to Ireland with a message and give it to an Abbot who is a friend of mine."

"Certainly," said Modemnoc politely, "but what about the Bees?"

"We'll look after them until you get back. They'll be all right," said David kindly.

"Well, don't forget to give them Syrup when the weather gets cold," said Modemnoc.

"No, we won't," said David.

So Modemnoc went down to the ship, and just as he was Going Aboard all the Bees came buzzing round in a Swarm, so that the sailors ran away in a fright.

"They won't hurt you!" said Modemnoc. "They only came to see me because I am going away from them." And he tried to shoo them back home, but they wouldn't go. So he turned and walked back to the Monastery, and all the Bees flew along with him, and when he got to the Garden they went gathering Honey in the flowers as though nothing had happened! Very Quietly Modemnoc slipped out of the garden and hurried back to the ship.

"They didn't see me go!" he said to himself, but just as he was Going Aboard all the Bees came buzzing round in a swarm, so that the sailors ran away in a fright! The sailors were very Angry because they were frightened, and although Modemnoc kept on saying how Sorry he was they said that if it happened again they would sail without him!

So Modemnoc went back again to the Monastery, and the Bees went too. He went to David, who said:

"Haven't you gone yet, Brother?"

"It's those Bees," said Modemnoc.

"What about them? I told you they would be all right," said David.

"Well," said Modemnoc in an Apologising voice, "they will keep coming after me, and the sailors are getting Furious."

"How Trying of them," said David. "What are you going to do about them?"

"I wondered if you would let me take them with me, please," said Modemnoc. "They wouldn't be any Trouble, really they wouldn't. I could take them in a Skep." (A Skep is one of those round Beehive things made of straw.)

"All right, if you think you can Manage them," said David. "But there's to be no Coming Out and Stinging the sailors, mind!"

"No, they'll keep quite Quiet, if you will please Bless them," said Modemnoc, and he smiled an Enormous Smile because he was so pleased.

So David blessed Modemnoc and the Bees, and the bees went into the Skep and the sailors never even knew that they were there! When they got to Ireland they started making Honey in the Skep, and the Irish people were All Astonished, because it was the first time they had ever seen Tame Bees in a Beehive.

Lots of other things happened to David, and I'll tell you One More.

When the Monks at Glastonbury, in England, had finished building their Famously Beautiful Chapel in their Monastery by St. Joseph's Thorn Tree they wrote and asked David to come and Dedicate it for them. Now you know all about Dedicating because I remember telling you about it before (I think it was in the Westminster Story, wasn't it?) but in case you have forgotten I will tell you again. When a Church is built it is given to Our Lord or to Our Lady or to a Saint so that it can be their Special Church to look after. That is why Churches are called St. Edmund's Church or St. James's Church or the Church of the Sacred Heart. (What is the name of the Church that you go to, do you know?) And it is always the Bishop who comes and Dedicates the Church. The Monks, of course, wanted their Church to be Dedicated to St. Joseph of Arimathea, and David was very pleased, because he loved Dedicating, and he said that he would come and do it to-morrow as he was in the Neighbourhood. That night Our Lord came to him when he was asleep and He said:

"You needn't Dedicate the Church to-morrow, David, because I have Dedicated it Myself."

David was so glad that Our Lord had come to see him that he quite forgot to be disappointed about not doing the Dedicating himself, but Our Kind Lord never forgets anything like that, and He said:

"I do know, David, that you love Dedicating, and the Monks have not built a Lady Chapel yet for their Beautiful Church. Will you build one on to the end of the Church and Dedicate it yourself to My Dear Mother?"

David was Delighted, and he spent a long time at Glastonbury building the Lady Chapel. And when it was finished he Dedicated it to Our Lady to be her Special Chapel. But I am afraid that you will never see it, because Cromwell's soldiers pulled it down and Smashed it up, together with the Famously Beautiful Church, because they said that beautiful things are Wicked. (But you know better than that.)

St. David's Special Day is on March 1st, and Thousands of people are called after him, not only in Wales.

ST. RONALD

ONCE upon a time there was an Earl of Orkney (The Orkneys are islands off the North of Scotland, where Scapa Flow and the Navy and all that are.) And this Earl of Orkney had a Favourite Granddaughter whose name was Gunnhild. Now lots of people wanted to marry Gunnhild, sometimes because she was an Earl's Granddaughter and sometimes because she was Very Pretty, but always the Earl said:

"No, m'dear, he's not good enough!"

"But," said poor Gunnhild, "if we go on like this, I'll never get married at all!"

"That's all right, m'dear," said the Earl, "I'll find somebody Suitable, don't you worry." And he tweaked Gunnhild's ear and ambled off to the Stable to look at his Retriever Puppies.

Then one day a Norwegian ship came sailing into Kirkwall (which is the capital of Orkney) and out stepped a Very Handsome Man with Red Hair. He called on the Earl and said:

"Good day, your Lordship. I came to ask if I may have the honour to Marry your Granddaughter."

"Eh! What's that?" said the Earl, "but I don't know anything about you. Who *are* you?"

"I am a Norwegian Nobleman," said the handsome visitor.

"Got any money?" asked the Earl, pulling his moustache.

"Yes," said the Handsome Norwegian Nobleman.

"Got a decent Place to live in?" asked the Earl, making a Fierce face.

"Yes," said the Handsome Norwegian Nobleman with Red Hair.

"I'll fetch the girl in to have a look at you, what?" said the Earl, and he trundled off to find Gunnhild.

When she saw the Handsome Norwegian Nobleman with Red Hair, Gunnhild thought that she'd never seen anybody that she'd rather have for a Husband, and so they were married at once, and they sailed back to Norway to her new home.

Soon they had a Son, and he was named Ronald, and he grew up in Norway, and was very Tall and Handsome, with Red Hair, just like his father's.

Ronald learned to Row and to Play the Harp, and to Play Darts, and to go on Snowshoes and to Ride a Horse and all sorts of other things. And he used to make up poetry about all the things that he could do. (That is how I know what he learned, because I've read some of the Poetry.)

One day, when he was Thirteen, Ronald sailed to Grimsby, in England, in a merchant ship, to see what it was like. They stayed there for Five Weeks, and poor Ronald thought that it was the most frightful place that he had ever seen. He wrote and told his Handsome Norwegian father that he waded in Mud, and that everything was dreadfully Dirty, and that he hoped he'd soon be sailing home on the clean grey Sea.

One summer Holiday Ronald had an Adventure, and this was it: He went with a friend of his, whose name was Karl, to a Seaside place called Trondheim, and there was a little Island there. So Ronald and Karl thought that they would go over to the Island for a Picnic.

"Don't you go," said an old Sailor, who was sitting on a bollard and staring out to sea.

"Why?" asked Ronald.

"A Giant lives there," said the sailor; "has done for years. Really wicked, he is. Eats all the people that go to the Island and keeps their money. He must have got Hundreds and Thousands of pounds of Treasure."

Ronald looked at Karl, and Karl looked at Ronald.

"Shall we go and find the Treasure?" they both said at once. Then they shook little fingers because of saying the same thing at the same time.

So in spite of the old sailor's Warning they took some food and some water and rowed across to the Island. Very quietly they went up the beach and found the Giant's Cave.

"He must be out Fishing, or something," whispered Ronald.

"I'll get a rope from the boat in case of Accidents," said Karl, "and we'll Explore the cave."

So, carrying the rope, they went Carefully into the cave. They went on and on, and further and further, until it was nearly Pitch Dark. Then Ronald, who was in front, stopped so suddenly that Karl bumped into him.

"Don't do that!" said Ronald in a fright.

"I couldn't help it," said Karl, Rather Crossly.

"Well, look what you nearly made me do!" said Ronald, and there stretching out in front of them was a Deep Dark lake in the cave!

"Now what do we do?" said Karl.

"Swim across," said Ronald; "I expect the Treasure is on the other side. I haven't seen any this side."

"Neither have I," said Karl.

So they took out their Torches and stuck them on to their heads with little pats of clay. Then they tied the rope between them. (They did that so that if one of them got Lost the other could find him.) Then they waded out into the Lake and began to swim to the Other Side. They swam on and on and on, and it got very Cold, but at last they got to the Other Side!

"Now for the Treasure!" said Ronald.

"Come on," said Karl, and then he stopped. "This is the End," he said.

"How do you mean, the End?" asked Ronald.

"The *End*," said Karl; "we can't get any further; it's the End of the Cave."

And so it was! So they looked and looked along the edge of the Lake for the treasure, but all they could find was a Very Nasty Smell. So they built a little heap of stones to show that they had been there, and then they swam back again. They went very Quietly out of the cave onto the beach, because of the Giant; but they never saw a Sign of him!

"Well," said Ronald, "that was a Lucky Escape!"

"Yes," said Karl, "there was No Giant, but what a shame that there was No Treasure either!"

Now when Ronald was older, what with Fighting and Pirates and so forth, most of his relations in Orkney were dead, and so the Earl's Castle was his. But his Cousin Paul, who lived there, wouldn't give it up.

So Ronald's Handsome Norwegian Father sent six ships full of soldiers and sailors, with Ronald in the Front Ship, to fight Paul and win the Earl's Castle in Orkney. So Ronald sailed away, and first he went to Shetland to meet a friend of his who had Twelve ships. But what with Wind and Weather he missed the friend, and had to go and fight Cousin Paul with only Six ships. And who do you suppose Won? No, Paul did! And Ronald lost all the six ships, and by the time he got back home to Norway his Handsome Father was *Furious* because of the Waste of good ships, as well as the soldiers and sailors.

Now Ronald was Absolutely Determined that he would win Orkney from his Cousin Paul, and so the next year he got some more ships and some more soldiers and sailors. But this time, before he started, he went to Church and talked for a long time to his Favourite Saint, whose name was St. Magnus.

"You see," he said to St. Magnus, "my Cousin Paul is a very Bad Ruler. He doesn't look after the people properly; he only thinks about making himself Rich. So I would be very Grateful if you would help me to take Orkney away from him, and then I can have it. After all, it is my own place!" And he made a Bargain with St. Magnus. (A Bargain is: If you do This, I'll do That.) And this was the Bargain that Ronald made with St. Magnus.

"If *you* help *me* to win the Battle with Cousin Paul, *I* will build a Stone Church (not just a brick one), in Kirkwall, which is the most Important town in Orkney, and the church will be Dedicated to *you*."

So then Ronald sailed away from Norway with his soldiers and sailors and fought with Cousin Paul, and this time he Won the Battle, and so he was the Earl of Orkney, like his Great Grandfather used to be.

As soon as he had got settled in his new Palace Ronald called all the best Carvers and Builders and Carpenters and all that and said:

"Now all you Builders and things, now is the time to build that Stone Church that I promised to St. Magnus. So will you please start the First Thing to-morrow morning."

And the Stone Masons cut the stone and the Carpenters cut the wood and the Carvers carved it, and the

Artists painted it, and there, in a very short time, was a lovely Stone Church in the town of Kirkwall, and it was Dedicated to St. Magnus. So if, one day, you go to Orkney, on Sunday morning you will go to Church in that very same church, and you will remember about Ronald and his Bargain.

Now Ronald did lots of other things, and one of them was Going to the Crusades. I expect you know what the Crusades were, but perhaps I had better remind you just in case:

All the places in Palestine where Our Lord lived are very Special because of His being Actually There. So Bethlehem is Special because He was Born there, and Nazareth is Special because the Holy Family lived there, and St. Joseph had his Shop there. (What sort of shop was it?) And the Sea of Galilee and Jerusalem and all those Places were Special. So of course all the Christians would want to have the Places for theirs, wouldn't they? But the Heathens and the Infidels (who don't believe that Our Lord was God, which, of course, He was) said:

"But *we* were there first, and we want to keep the Places, and you can't have Chapels and things because the places are not Special for us!" And they made Hotels and Market Places and things on the most Special Places of all, just to show what they thought about them.

So all the Christian Kings and Lords like the French King and the Spanish King and the English King and the Earl of Orkney and the German Princess collected their soldiers to Win Back the Holy Places from the Heathens and the Infidels. (Now this was at first a Very Good Thing, but in the end it turned into Anybody's Fight.)

So Ronald said to the Bishop of Orkney:

"I will go to the Crusades and help to save the Holy

Places from the Infidels. Especially Bethlehem, because I can't bear Infidels spoiling the place where Our Lord was born."

And the Bishop said:

"Good. I will go with you."

But when Ronald wanted to collect Knights and Soldiers to go with him there weren't enough. (Because if he took *all* the soldiers Cousin Paul might come back and Capture Orkney again.) So he went to Norway, where his Handsome Father and Gunnhild, his Mother, lived, and he collected some Knights and Soldiers from there. When they got back to Orkney it was Winter, and much too cold to start, so they waited for the Spring. But the Norwegian soldiers were very Noisy and Tiresome, and the Bishop had to make a Speech to them and tell them to behave properly.

"Really," said the Bishop, "anyone would think that you were a Heathen Viking Expedition and not a Crusade at all!"

One man was especially Tiresome. His name was Thorbion Klerk, and he used to set haystacks on fire. When all the people Rushed Out to put out the fire, he used to Rush Into their houses and steal everything Valuable. He got so Rich that some wicked but not so brave men joined with him, and they were a Positive Menace. So Ronald sat on his Earl's Throne and sent for Thorbion Klerk.

When he came Ronald said:

"Thorbion Klerk, you are one of my Subjects, and you are no better than any other Subject, so why do you Steal and Burn and start Riots in my peaceful Orkney?"

But Thorbion Klerk was Stubborn, and he wouldn't answer.

"Very well," said Ronald, "then I won't have you for

a Subject any longer. You will be a Public Enemy, and if *anyone* does *anything* to you I won't put them in Prison."

Thorbion Klerk was very Angry, but he couldn't say anything, and he had to go away and hide because of being an Outlaw.

Then Ronald and his Crusaders sailed away to the Holy Land, and Ronald fought very Bravely and very Hard for a time, but he spent more and more time visiting all the places where Our Lord went, so his Knights thought that they might just as well go home, and some of them did. Ronald saw all the places again and again, and by seeing them so often and by thinking about Our Lord so much, he stopped wanting to fight, and he wanted to go home and tell all his people what all the places were like. So he sailed home, and when he landed in Orkney, crowds and crowds of his people came to meet him, and they Clapped and Cheered and Sang and the Band played, and Ronald climbed up on a wall and told them all about the things that he had seen. All the people were very Interested because they had never seen anybody who had actually Been to the Holy Land and Seen all the Holy Places. Then Ronald got off the wall and started to walk up to the Village to get a Horse to ride home to Kirkwall on, and all the crowd went with him, cheering and bumping up against him.

Suddenly a Terrible Thing happened. All in the middle of the General Rejoicing Ronald fell down dead! And this was why:

In all the crowd nobody saw the Wicked Thorbion Klerk, and he got nearer and nearer to Ronald, until at last he Stabbed him and Killed him because of being an Outlaw.

So the happy crowd turned into a sad crowd, and they

picked up Ronald and put him into a ship all decorated in Black and Purple, because they are such Sad Colours, and they made a Procession of Ships and Boats, and they sailed round to Kirkwall singing Sad Songs and Playing Sad Music. Now the people in Kirkwall had heard that Earl Ronald had come home, and they were all getting ready for a Glad Party to welcome him, and when they saw the Sad Procession of ships they couldn't think who it could be, and they went down to the Sea to wait. When the ships landed all the people cried, and were as sad as sad, because they had liked Ronald very much, and he had only just come home. They took him and buried him in the Stone Church that he had built for St. Magnus, and it was a long time before they had a Ruler that they loved so much.

St. Ronald's Special Day is on August 20th, and hundreds of people can have him for their Special Saint, because there are hundreds of Ronalds.

ST. JOSEPH OF ARIMATHEA .

ONCE upon a time there was a man who was a Good and Just Counsellor, and his name was Joseph, and he lived in a place called Arimathea, and he was one of Our Lord's Disciples. (A Disciple is a person who follows and learns from another person. Our Lord had hundreds of Disciples, but only Twelve Apostles.) We don't really know very much about Joseph, except that he was a Nobleman and Rich, but I'll tell you what we do know. After Our Lord had been crucified and had died the Roman soldiers just left Him on the Cross. The Disciples thought what a terrible thing this was, and how dreadful for Our Lady, too, but they were afraid of the Roman soldiers, and of the Jews who had wanted Our Lord to be crucified, and so they didn't do anything about it. So, late in the evening, Joseph, because he was Rich and therefore Important, went secretly (so that the Romans and the Jews wouldn't know) to Pontius Pilate and asked him Please could he take away Our Lord's Body to bury it? Now Pilate hadn't really wanted to crucify Our Lord at all, and he was feeling very sorry about it, but he did not believe that Our Lord could be dead yet. He thought that Joseph was trying to help Him to escape. So he sent for the Centurion, whose name was Longinus, and he asked him if it was true that Our Lord was dead. Longinus said, "Yes, I saw Him die." Then Pilate said that Joseph could take away the Body and bury it.

So Joseph and another Disciple called Nicodemus took Our Lord's Body down from the Cross. Now Joseph's garden was near the place where He was crucified, and in the garden was a new cave in the rock that Joseph had got ready for himself to be buried in when he died. By the time they had got Our Lord down it was very late at night, and he did not know of anywhere else near at hand, so he hoped that his own new cave would be nice enough for Our Lord, and he thanked God for the honour of being allowed to give it up. So Joseph and Nicodemus put Our Lord's Body safely there, and they rolled a great Rock to the door of the cave so that no one could get in in the Night. Then they went sadly home. Now all that is perfectly true, but there are lots of other stories about the things that Joseph did afterwards that are not in the Bible, and I will tell you some of them.

A year after Joseph had given his own new cave to be a burial place for Our Lord, St. Philip, who was one of the Apostles, sent Joseph and eleven of his friends to England to tell the English people about Our Lord. Because, of course, there were no Christians there yet, and no one had even Heard of such a thing.

Now there were a lot of Tin Mines in Cornwall (and there still are) and people used to come from round about Palestine to buy Tin. So Joseph and his Eleven Friends sailed in one of the Tin people's boats, and after a time they landed in Cornwall, which is in the bottom left-hand corner of England. They brought with them a very Precious Thing. It was the Silver Cup that Our Lord had used at the Last Supper when He put wine into it and said, "THIS IS MY BLOOD." Do you remem· ber? The cup was called the Holy Grail.

Lots of people collected round to Stare at Joseph and his Eleven Friends, because they had different Clothes and they could not speak English. But they went on to a place nearby, to Glastonbury, and they made a Camp, and they settled down and got friendly with the people, and soon they could speak English fairly well.

Everyone who used to visit their camp used to look at their Chapel and say:

"What's that place?"

"It's a Chapel."

"What's a Chapel?" asked the Visitor.

"A place where we Worship God," said Joseph.

"Can I see?" asked the Visitor.

"Of course you can," said Joseph.

And always, when they went into the Chapel and saw the Holy Grail, the people would want to know about it, and Joseph or one of his Eleven Friends would tell them. But they were not allowed to touch the Holy Grail, because of it being so Precious. And so, because they couldn't *see* the Christians' God, some of the English people thought that He must be in the Cup.

"That's why Joseph won't let us touch it," they said.

"Well," said one of them, "let's Steal it just for one day, and then we'll be able to see God."

After that so many of the English people tried to get into the Chapel, and so often, that the Christians had to take it in Turns to Stand Guard, and at last Joseph said to them:

"We can't go on like this. One of these days somebody really will Steal the Holy Grail, and it is much too Precious to be handed round the Villages for everyone to Stare at and Handle. What do you all think that we had better do?"

They thought and they wondered, and at last one of them said:

"Couldn't we Bury it in a Safe Place?"

The others all thought that this was a very good Idea, and so they buried the Holy Grail by a well at the bot-

tom of a little mountain called Glastonbury Tor. It was
a winter's day and Joseph stuck his tall Walking Stick
into the ground to Mark the Place. And now a wonderful
thing happened! You remember that it was a Winter's
day? Well, the walking stick grew Roots and Leaves and
Flowers and turned into a Hawthorn Tree all in the

The walking stick grew Roots and Leaves and Flowers.

same afternoon! And what is more, instead of flowering
every Summer like Hawthorns always do, it flowered
every Winter!

Well Joseph travelled on and taught the people about
being Christians, and they built them Chapels, and they
never got back to Glastonbury, somehow. Nobody else
knew where the Grail was buried, and they thought that
the Hawthorn Tree was Joseph's Stick, and that it was

very Surprising, but they never thought that it was Marking anything.

But for Hundreds of years people looked and searched for the Holy Grail. It was one of those Special Things that King Arthur's Knights of the Round Table tried to do, and one of them, called Sir Galahad, is supposed to have seen it once, but we don't know if he really did, because it is all so very Long Ago. But as far as we know, it never has been found. Or perhaps somebody found it and never knew what a Precious Thing it was.

Anyway, after years and years some Monks came and built a Monastery, with a Famously Beautiful Chapel, round Joseph's Thorn Tree so that it was in their Garden and they looked after it for Ages until it got Very old. At last one of the Gardening Monks said to the Abbot:

"Father Abbot, I am afraid that St. Joseph's Thorn Tree won't live much longer. It is Hundreds of years old. Do you suppose that I might take one or two Cuttings so that we'll still have some of it when the Old Tree dies?"

"I don't see why not," said the Abbot, rubbing his chin with his thumb. "It would be a great Pity to lose it altogether after All these Years."

So the Brother Gardener made Two or Three Cuttings, and they had just started to grow nicely when Oliver Cromwell's soldiers arrived!

I don't know if you know about Oliver Cromwell, but he was one of the Heads of the Puritans who were Extraordinary people, and they only thought Three Things.

One was that they thought that the Church was Bad, and that all the Beautiful Churches were Bad too.

Two, they thought that Kings were Bad to have.

Three, they thought people couldn't be Happy as well as Good, and that Sundays must be Solemn and Sad, and that Churches must be Plain and Ugly, and that nobody must Laugh or Sing (because you couldn't be Good as well as Happy) and Worst of All they thought God was terrible and Frightening, and was always watching to see if He could Catch you out.

So you can see what Extraordinary people they were, can't you? (As a Matter of Fact there are still some of them about, poor, miserable things.)

Well, Cromwell's soldiers went about Smashing the lovely old Churches and Burning them. Haven't you seen Statues and things in old Churches with their noses bashed and their fingers broken off? Well, now you know who did it.

When the soldiers got to Glastonbury they pulled down the Famously Beautiful Church, and then they went into the Monastery Garden and saw the Thorn Tree.

"What's this?" they shouted. "St. Joseph's Thorn? Nonsense, of *course* it can't flower in the Winter! What Wickedness to tell such lies to the poor people!" And they Chopped it down and dug up the roots and made a Bonfire of the whole lot! *But* they didn't find the little Cuttings that the Brother Gardener had made!

So we still have St. Joseph's Thorn Tree. And one or two Cuttings have grown at Kew Gardens, so that all will be well if anything happens to the one in Glastonbury. And it really does flower in the Winter!

St. Joseph of Arimathea's Special Day is on March 17th, and anyone born on that day can have him for their Special Saint, specially people who live in Glastonbury.

ST. GLADYS

ONCE upon a time there was a Rich Pagan and his beautiful wife, and they had a daughter called Gladys, and they lived at Brecknock, in Wales, a very long time ago. All the people in those days were very Fierce and Warlike. Not the sort of War that we have nowadays, but Villages fought Battles against Villages and Towns against Towns, and even Families against Families!

Supposing that your father didn't like Mr. Prodgrub, who lives down the road, and Mr. Prodgrub couldn't bear your father. And supposing one day that your father said:

"Come on, chaps! I'm going to have a crack at that old Prodgrub. I can't stand the sight of him any longer!" And Supposing that your father took his Gardening Fork and your mother took her Umbrella and all you children took pokers and trowels and tins of water and things, and the cook and the gardener and the Village people who liked your father best all brought things to Poke and Hit Mr. Prodgrub, and you all went down the road and Attacked Mr. Prodgrub's house! And supposing all the Prodgrubs and their friends fought back. It would be like a proper Battle, and people might get Killed, and most certainly some of them would get Hurt. And supposing that your father Won, and you all went into Mr. Prodgrub's house and took away all the things that you had always wanted and you put them in your own house to make it look nicer! Well, that is the sort of thing that was always happening when Gladys was a girl. And the next week probably the Prodgrubs would come and take back their things and some of yours, too. And so it would go on.

One day a Swashbuckling man called Gundleus saw Gladys, and he thought that she was so beautiful in her Rich Silk Dress that he went to her Rich Pagan Father and said:

"Good morning, Sir; I have come to ask you if I can have your daughter's Hand in Marriage."

"Well, you can't have it, see?" said the Rich Pagan Father rudely.

"I *do* want her for my Wife," said the swashbuckling Gundleus sadly.

"You heard what I said," said the Rich Pagan Father. "Now go away!" And he slammed the door in Gundleus' face!

Poor Gundleus felt Sad, and then he felt Angry. The more he thought about it the Angrier he got, until at last he Muttered to himself:

"Of all the Rude, Unmannerly, Discourteous Abominations I ever saw, that man is the Worst!" And he got all Red and Swashbuckling, and he went home and collected Three Hundred friends and relations, and they all marched back to Gladys's house and Attacked it. Gladys's Rich Pagan Father was taken by surprise, and when Gundleus had got into the house he found Gladys gossiping with her sisters in the Garden.

"Come on, quick!" he said to Gladys, pulling her hand.

"Why!" said Gladys, and she dropped her knitting because she was so Fussed.

"I want to Marry you," said Gundleus.

"Oh, all right," said Gladys.

And she jumped up onto the horse that Gundleus had brought for her and they galloped away with all the

Three Hundred friends and relations, and a fine Clatter they made.

As soon as he had Pulled himself Together the Rich Pagan Father collected *his* friends and relations to chase after the others. When he saw that there was going to be a Battle, Gundleus put Gladys to ride beside him in the

. . . they galloped away.

most Dangerous Place, so that her father wouldn't Attack them in case Gladys was Killed.

At last they got to Vochriw, which was where Gundleus lived. And there, sitting on the very Top of the Hill, there happened to be King Arthur and two of his Knights of the Round Table, who were playing Dice. When King Arthur looked down to the bottom of the Hill and saw Gladys riding by he was quite Overcome.

"I have never seen such a Beautiful Girl in all my life!" he said to his two Knights. "I want her for my own!"

"But she belongs to Gundleus," said one of the Knights. "Look at him riding with her!"

"Then let us go down to the bottom of the Hill and take her away from Gundleus," said King Arthur, who was feeling a bit Possessive.

The Knights didn't think that this was a very Good Idea, because Gundleus still had his Three Hundred people with him, you remember, and there were only two of them! But everyone has to do what the King says, and they didn't know how to get out of it. At last one of them had a Plan.

"Well, Your Majesty," he said, "we could easily take her away if we were in your country. But this is Gundleus's country and, actually, we are Trespassers. I should *think*," said the Knight, rattling the Dice Box gently, "that we might be Prosecuted if we took her away from Gundleus in his own country."

But King Arthur was still Entranced as he stared at Gladys, and he was just going down the Hill himself when the other Knight said:

"Just a minute, Your Majesty! You know that everybody, especially Foreigners, thinks that you and your Knights are the very Acme of Chivalry, and that you always help the Needy?"

"Yes, of course I do!" said King Arthur with a Pleased Smile.

"*Well*," said the Knight, "I just thought that it would make a Better Impression if we helped Gundleus and his friends against the people who are chasing them."

"So it would!" said King Arthur, and he peered at

the Rich Pagan Father, "What a very Unpleasant-looking gentleman that is in the Front!"

And King Arthur and his two Knights hurried down the Hill so fast that the Rich Pagan Father thought that there must be lots more Knights behind the Hill. So he and his followers rode home as fast as they could, and King Arthur and Gundleus shook hands at the bottom of the Hill and said Good Afternoon to each other, and King Arthur had a good look at Gladys because of her being so beautiful.

So Gladys and Gundleus got married (in a Pagan church) and they lived very happily in Gundleus's castle, and they did a lot of Fighting and some of Gundleus's ships went Pirating, and they got very Rich. Then they had a son called Cadoc.

Now Cadoc wasn't the Swashbuckling sort at all, and he never wanted to Pirate or to Raid or to Loot or to Wreak Havoc in the country round about like Gladys and Gundleus loved doing, and when he went away to finish his Education he became a Christian.

Gladys and Gundleus were terribly Disappointed! Such a thing had never happened in the Family before! They thought for some peculiar reason that Christians were Meek and Mild (which is a milk-and-watery sort of thing to be and not Christian at all). "However," said Gundleus, "what's done's done and we must just put up with it I suppose!"

One day when they were sitting round the fire after tea, Gladys was refooting some stockings for Cadoc, and Gundleus was rubbing his dog's ears, and Cadoc was sorting Trout Flies, Gundleus said:

"It's very Dull just now, isn't it? We haven't had a Good Fight for weeks!"

"Yes," said Gladys, "what about Attacking the house

along the River; they've got some good horses that I should like. Just pick up my wool for me, will you, dear?"

Gundleus picked it up, and Cadoc said:

"Why Attack them?"

And Gladys said:

"Well, we always do Attack someone don't we, dear?"

And Cadoc said:

"Yes, and they Attack you."

"Ah," said Gundleus, "but that is because they don't like us, not because they are Swashbuckling Freebooters like we are."

"If you didn't Attack them they'd like you," said Cadoc; "you are very nice people, really."

"But we *must* fight *something*," said Gladys; "we always do."

"Couldn't you perhaps fight the Devil and all God's enemies?" said Cadoc, taking out some March Browns and putting them aside for to-morrow.

"Who is God?" said Gladys. (Did you remember that she was a Pagan?)

And Cadoc told them about God and Lucifer and the Battle in Heaven and all that. You know the story, don't you?

"So," he said, "you could easily fight *and* be Christians if you fight the people who are not on God's side. Only, of course, you must be sure, first, which *is* God's side. The Church can always tell you that if you are not Quite Sure."

Gundleus said that nothing would Induce him to be a Christian, and he went on about it so much that Gladys said:

"Well, dear, I feel inclined to trust our Son, so that

when we get to Heaven he will be a Father to us because he knows so much more about it than we do."

So they went to a priest that Cadoc knew, and were Baptised, and were Christians. And they got to know God very well, and were terribly sad that they hadn't known him before.

They became so good at fighting Battles with the Devil that everybody loved them, and they each built a Church so that would help in making up for all their years of Swashbuckling. Gladys built one at Pencarn, in Monmouthshire, and Gundleus built one at Newport.

After a very long time Gundleus died when he was an old man, and Gladys was a Widow. So she went to live in a little house by herself on a cliff just above the bridge over the river Ebbw. There is a spring of very cold water near her house, and she bathed in it every day, Summer and Winter, and everyone was Astonished because she was an Old Lady and yet she never caught a Cold.

St. Gladys's Special Day is on March 29, and there are lots of people called Gladys in Wales and out of Wales, too.